KT-465-308

THE
PAUL HAMLYN
LIBRARY

DONATED BY
THE PAUL HAMLYN
FOUNDATION
TO THE
BRITISH MUSEUM

WITHDRAWN

opened December 2000

Kipling on Horses and Horsemen

Kipling
on
Horses
and
Horsemen

Selected and Introduced
by
John Welcome

MARLBOROUGH/PUNCHESTOWN

MARLBOROUGH BOOKS
6 Milton Road, Swindon, Wilts SN1 5JG
c/o 9 Queen Street, Melbourne 3000, Victoria, Australia

PUNCHESTOWN BOOKS
Ormond Court, 11 Lower Ormond Quay, Dublin 1

First published 1992

© Preface/Introductions John Welcome

ACKNOWLEDGMENT
Grateful acknowledgment is made to The Oxford University
Press for permission to reprint the notes to the verses
'At The Distance', 'Ichabod' and 'The Ballad of Ahmed Shah'
which appeared in *Early Verse by Rudyard Kipling* 1879–1889
published by The Clarendon Press in 1986 and was edited by
Andrew Rutherford.

THANKS
I would like to thank Ian Hannah for help in preparing this volume
and the loan of the book his father wrote, *Bobs Kipling's General*.

Typesetting and Origination Footnote Graphics, Warminster.

Jacket Design *Ron Stephens*.

ISBN 1–873919–05–0 Marlborough
ISBN 1–873920–03–2 Punchestown

Printed and Bound in England
by Loader Jackson Printers
Arlesey, Bedfordshire SG15 6XD

CONTENTS

PREFACE

All his life Rudyard Kipling hero-worshipped men of action and longed to be one of them – the men who rode horses, polo players and gentlemen riders, who ranked perhaps highest in the pantheon of his heroes. Unquestionably it was the greatest of regrets and disappointments in a life full of unhappiness, personal tragedy and ghastly ill-health that he never could fulfil this ambition. Small, short-sighted and awkward in movement, Kipling was inept at all games and an indifferent horseman. None of these things, however, prevented him writing of horsemen and horses supremely well.

"He had early in life," the second Lord Birkenhead, one of his many biographers wrote, "formed a preference for the men of action to the men of ideas," and it is the case that this preference stayed with him to the end of his career. Always he avoided the company of intellectuals and literati, preferring the racecourse, the polo ground, the club and the mess to the salon, the gallery and the literary tea. And that, undoubtedly, is one of the reasons, and possibly the greatest, that from that day to this the intelligentsia, savagely led by the epicene Max Beerbohm, have so vitriolically attacked him.

"Come back with me to the North and be amongst men once more", was a sentiment hardly likely in the closing years of the last century to appeal to the "Greenery yallery, Grosvenor Gallery" literary clique of that day who were satirised by Gilbert in *Patience* and who dominated the reading public of the time. This did not prevent Kipling's works being eagerly snapped up by those in whose paths he would have chosen to tread.

In compiling this collection I have kept as far as possible to chronological order and followed Kipling's practice in many of his own short stories of prefacing and post-scripting the stories with verses which seemed appropriate to their time and theme. I have also added where it appeared relevant without being impertinent introductory notes to explain something of their provenance and how he garnered the ideas and circumstances which inspired them. All in one way or another concern the horse and its effects on the lives of those of whom he wrote, for after all did he not say:

> "Four things greater than all things are
> Women and Horses and Power and War"?

1

★ THE MARE'S NEST
★ THE BALLAD OF AHMED SHAH

These are *vers de société* written originally for *The Civil and Military Gazette* and other papers from the heyday of the Raj when Kipling, then aged twenty-one, was working on the paper as his editor and patron, E. Kay Robinson, who first divined his genius, put it, "Like a blood-horse between the shafts." The young Kipling, peering short-sightedly through his thick glasses saw everything in that closed society, heard more than he saw and forgot nothing. Picking up the gossip of club, cantonment and racecourse he turned it into wickedly pointed light verse. Well could he say with Robbie Burns, "A chiel's amang ye takin' notes and, faith, he'll prent it.!"

These were the rhymes which set all British India chuckling. Everyone knew who was what in them and the stories behind them. They loved and revelled in the worldly "knowingness" with which the young man of twenty-one, who looked fifteen years older and who appeared to have reached advanced maturity when in his early teens, set it all down. Those in that closed society involved with horses – as, indeed nearly everyone then was, delighted in the two stanzas from *Certain Mazims of Hafiz* which carried a warning and put into verse what they all thought:

"As the thriftless gold of the *babul* so is the gold
that we spend

7

"On a Derby Sweep, or a neighbour's wife, or the
    horse that we bought from a friend.
"The ways of a man with a maid be strange, yet
    simple and tame
"To the ways of a man with a horse, when selling
    or racing that same."

As to who the "Hafiz" was from whom these maxims were
purportedly translated only Kipling knew and he never told
since it was undoubtedly himself. They may however have
owed something to his conversations with the mysterious
Pathan, Mahub Ali, who visited him regularly and whom he
cross-examined at length and in detail about life beyond his
own boundaries. In any event they struck a chord and were
widely quoted in stable, mess and club. Indeed, as Lord
Birkenhead says in his biography: "Men in the army, the
Civil Service and The Railway wrote to Kipling saying his
verses had penetrated as far as Rangoon, Moulmein and
Mandalay," and while some smarted others chuckled since,
as another writer of the time said, "in India a man's private
life was never exclusively his own." Kipling himself wrote of
this early work to his friend Mrs Hill:

'And some are truth and some are lie,
    And some exactly half and half,
I heard some made a woman cry –
    I *know* some made a woman laugh.'

THE MARE'S NEST

Jane Austen Beecher Stowe de Rouse
    Was good beyond all earthly need;
But, on the other hand, her spouse
    Was very, very bad indeed,
He smoked cigars, called churches slow,
And raced — but this she did not know.

8

For Belial Machiavelli kept
   The little fact a secret, and,
Though o'er his minor sins she wept,
   Jane Austen did not understand
That Lilly — thirteen-two and bay —
Absorbed one-half her husband's pay.

She was so good she made him worse
   (Some women are like this, I think);
He taught her parrot how to curse,
   Her Assam monkey how to drink.
He vexed her righteous soul until
She went up, and he went down hill.

Then came the crisis, strange to say,
   Which turned a good wife to a better.
A telegraphic peon, one day,
   Brought her — now, had it been a letter
For Belial Machiavelli, I
Know Jane would just have let it lie —

But 'twas a telegram instead,
   Marked "urgent," and her duty plain
To open it. Jane Austen read: —
   "Your Lilly's got a cough again.
" 'Can't understand why she is kept
"At your expense." Jane Austen wept.

It was a misdirected wire,
   Her husband was at Shaitanpore,
She spread her anger, hot as fire,
   Through six thin foreign sheets or more;
Sent off that letter, wrote another
To her solicitor — and mother.

Then Belial Machiavelli saw
   Her error and, I trust, his own,
Wired to the minion of the Law,
   And travelled wifeward — not alone.
For Lilly — thirteen-two and bay —
Came in a horse-box all the way.

There was a scene — a weep or two —
  With many kisses. Austen Jane
Rode Lilly all the season through,
  And never opened wires again.
She races now with Belial . . . This
Is very sad, but so it is.

THE BALLAD OF AHMED SHAH

This is the ballad of Ahmed Shah
Dealer in tats in the Sudder Bazar,
By the gate that leads to the Gold Minār,
How he was done by a youth from Morar.

Ahmed Shah was a man of peace —
His beard and his turban were thick with grease:
His paunch was huge and his speech was slow
And he swindled the subalterns high and low,
Scores of subalterns came to try
The tats that he sold — and remained to buy,
Scores of subalterns later on
Found that their flashiest mounts were 'gone' —
Some in the front and some behind
Some were roarers and some went blind —
Scores of subalterns over their 'weeds'
Cursed old Ahmed and all his deeds.
But Ahmed Shah in his gully sat still —
And ever he fashioned a *Little Black Pill*!

Yet a judgment was brewing for Ahmed Shah,
Like a witch's cauldron, in far Morar
And the youth that brewed it had eyes of blue
And his cheek was beardless — and boundless too.
Softly he mused o'er a trichi thick: —
'By the Beard of the Prophet I've got the trick!'
Then he rose from his chair with an artless grin

10

And called the Battery Sergeant in: —
'Sergeant' he said 'Hast aught for me
In the way of a "caster" with lots of gee?"
The sergeant pondered and answered slow
'There's a red-roan gelding that's bound to go
At the next Committee. 'E aint no use
Excep' for kickin' recruits to the deuce,
'E's chained in the sick-lines.'
                                    The subaltern's brow
Was puckered with thought for a moment. Then
The sergeant was richer by rupees ten.
'When the next Committee sits' quoth he
'O Sergeant buy up that brute for me.'

So the plot was laid and the long weeks passed
And the red-roan gelding was duly cast.
They led him in chains to the subaltern's stall
And gave him his gram' through a hole in the wall.
The subaltern mixed it. When morning came
The red-roan gelding was strangely tame.
He bit not nor kicked nor essayed to slay
And he and the sub went north that day
Till they came to the gully of Ahmed Shah
The man and the horse from far Morar.
The subaltern stated his funds were low
And he came — *mehrbáni* — to 'sell *karo*'.
Then Ahmed Shah with his eyes agog
Broke the Tenth Command in the decalogue
For the roan was a monster of size and thews
And stood over sixteen hand in his shoes.
'*Sahib kitna mangta*?' With brow serene,
The subaltern softly answered '*Teen*'.
He haggled an hour that dealer thrifty
Till the price was lowered to '*do sow fifty*'
And the money was paid in greasy rupees
While the red-roan gelding drowsed at his ease.
The subaltern left him — and Ahmed smiled —
'By Allah, how mad is this pink-faced child
I will stuff that *ghorah* with *atta* and *goor*

11

And sell him again to some English *soor*
For a clear eight-fifty!' . . . and e'en as he spoke
The devil they'd drugged in the red-roan woke!
Then the head-ropes snapped and the heel-ropes drew
And the stallions squealed as the roan went through
And the saices ran as men run for life
And the yard was troubled with equine strife
Till the berserk-rage of the beast was o'er
And he dropped to slumber at Ahmed's door!

Then a veil was lifted from Ahmed's eyes
As he raised the eyelids and punched the thighs
Felt the tense pulse slacken — the muscles still —
And fathomed the Trick of the Opium Pill!
His own old dodge that had brought him pelf
Had the subaltern turned against himself!

Did he swear? though his three best tats were lame
And half the city would hear of his shame.
Did he seek the law-courts? With down-cast eye
He hailed an ekka that jingled by,
And drove to the Station where, filled with peace
The subaltern counted the greasy rupees.

What passed between them? I cannot say
The subaltern turns the question away
With an innocent laugh: but the men of Morar
Say he still gets ponies from Ahmed Shah.
Ponies to bet on — but not to buy —
Weeds to look at but devils to fly
And one in a while comes a tiny pill-box
Which the subaltern puts in his private till-box.
The Doctor abets him . . . Whenever I'm able
I plunge to my last clean shirt on their stable!

2

★ THE BROKEN LINK HANDICAP ★ ICHABOD ★ AT THE DISTANCE ★ CHAPTER HEADINGS

In a recent study of Kipling and his work which is a searching examination into the Freudian roots of his genius which do not concern us here, Martin Seymour-Smith who is, on the whole, a far from friendly critic, nevertheless, called *The Broke Link Handicap* 'a mini-masterpiece'. So it is and it is well set off by his racing rhymes *Ichabod*, *At The Distance* and his *Chapter Headings* which I have included as an afterword to the story. In *At The Distance*, which is an account from the saddle of the riding of a gymkhana race and a slight case of skulduggery, the young Kipling demonstrated that he could hold his own in this difficult genre with such acknowledged masters of those who wrote and rode as Adam Lindsay Gordon and A. B. 'Banjo' Paterson.

It was this story and these verses which brought Kipling the admiration and appreciation of cavalry subalterns and gentlemen riders. "Where does the youngster pick it all up?" Bobby Pringle, a sporting vet who afterwards became a close friend, asked Kay Robinson in the club after he had read *At The Distance*. He was so complimentary about it that Kipling copied out for him, in his own hand, *The Ballad of Ahmed Shah*.

It has to be said, however, that *The Broken Link Handicap* did not escape criticism from another quarter on a point upon which Kipling prided himself – his mastery of technical detail. Five years after the first publication of the story in book form Kipling visited Melbourne. His regard for Australia and Australians, never very strong, cannot have been increased when he heard on landing that *Plain Tales From The Hills* in which *The Broken Link Handicap* appeared, had been banned from the Melbourne public library on the grounds of impropriety! Nor can it have been furthered if he had read the letter which Rolf Bolderwood, author of the classic of the outback and bushranging, *Robbery Under Arms*, addressed to his publishers. In the letter Bolderwood says: "He speaks of the 'Marybong Plate' (a *two-year-old* race) as a *dangerous steeplechase* with *jarrah* logs for jumps – which would have to be brought from Western Australia, 2,000 miles or so! He confuses the 'smash' which so affected the boy's nerve with that of the Caulfield Cup, *also a flat race*. However, this mistake apart, I have nothing but sincere admiration for him, prose and verse." Well might Mr Bolderwood have added that final rider, for the story the original of which was almost certainly written in haste for *The Civil and Military Gazette* as a filler and one which Kipling omitted to check, as indeed he sometimes did later on, remains, as Mr Seymour-Smith has said, a mini-masterpiece of its kind. It is perhaps worth adding that on his arrival in Australia Kipling was asked to attend The Melbourne Cup and report it. He refused.

THE BROKEN-LINK HANDICAP

While the snaffle holds, or the long-neck stings,
While the big beam tilts, or the last bell rings,
While horses are horses to train and to race,
Then women and wine take a second place
    For me – for me –
    While a short 'ten-three'
Has a field to squander or fence to face!
                Song of the G. R.

There are more ways of running a horse to suit your book than pulling his head off in the straight. Some men forget this. Understand clearly that all racing is rotten – as everything connected with losing money must be. In India, in addition to its inherent rottenness, it has the merit of being two-thirds sham; looking pretty on paper only. Every one knows every one else far too well for business purposes. How on earth can you rack and harry and post a man for his losings, when you are fond of his wife, and live in the same Station with him? He says, "On the Monday following," "I can't settle just yet." You say, "All right, old man," and think yourself lucky if you pull off nine hundred out of a two-thousand-rupee debt. Any way you look at it, Indian racing is immoral, and expensively immoral. Which is much worse. If a man wants your money, he ought to ask for it, or send round a subscription-list, instead of juggling about the country, with an Australian larrikin; a "brumby," with as much breed as the boy; a brace of *chumars* in gold-laced caps; three or four *ekka*-ponies with hogged manes, and a switch-tailed demirep of a mare called Arab because she has a kink in her flag. Racing leads to the *shroff* quicker than anything else. But if you have no conscience and no sentiments, and good hands, and some knowledge of pace, and ten years' experience of horses, and several thousand rupees a month, I believe that you can occasionally contrive to pay your shoeing-bills.

Did you ever know Shackles – b. w. g., 15. 1⅜ – coarse, loose, mule-like ears – barrel as long as a gatepost – tough as a telegraph-wire – and the queerest brute that ever looked through a bridle? He was of no brand, being one of an ear-nicked mob taken into the *Bucephalus* at £4:10s. a head to make up freight, and sold raw and out of condition at Calcutta for Rs.275. People who lost money on him called him a "brumby"; but if ever any horse had Harpoon's shoulders and The Gin's temper, Shackles was that horse. Two miles was his own particular distance. He trained himself, ran himself, and rode himself; and, if his jockey insulted him by giving him hints, he shut up at once and bucked the boy off. He objected to dictation. Two or three of his owners did not understand this, and lost money in consequence. At last he

15

was bought by a man who discovered that, if a race was to be won, Shackles, and Shackles only, would win it in his own way, so long as his jockey sat still. This man had a riding-boy called Brunt – a lad from Perth, West Australia – and he taught Brunt, with a trainer's whip, the hardest thing a jock can learn – to sit still, to sit still, and to keep on sitting still. When Brunt fairly grasped this truth, Shackles devastated the country. No weight could stop him at his own distance; and the fame of Shackles spread from Ajmir in the South, to Chedputter in the North. There was no horse like Shackles, so long as he was allowed to do his work in his own way. But he was beaten in the end; and the story of his fall is enough to make angels weep.

At the lower end of the Chedputter race-course just before the turn into the straight, the track passes close to a couple of old brick-mounds enclosing a funnel-shaped hollow. The big end of the funnel is not six feet from the railings on the off-side. The astounding peculiarity of the course is that, if you stand at one particular place, about half a mile away, inside the course, and speak at ordinary pitch, your voice just hits the funnel of the brick-mounds and makes a curious whining echo there. A man discovered this one morning by accident while out training with a friend. He marked the place to stand and speak from with a couple of bricks, and he kept his knowledge to himself. *Every* peculiarity of a course is worth remembering in a country where rats play the mischief with the elephant-litter, and Stewards build jumps to suit their own stables. This man ran a very fairish country-bred, a long, racking high mare with the temper of a fiend, and the paces of an airy wandering seraph – a drifty, glidy stretch. The mare was, as a delicate tribute to Mrs. Reiver, called "The Lady Regula Baddun" – or for short, Regula Baddun.

Shackles' jockey, Brunt, was a quite well-behaved boy, but his nerve had been shaken. He began his career by riding jump-races in Melbourne, where a few Stewards want lynching, and was one of the jockeys who came through the awful butchery – perhaps you will recollect it – of the Maribyrnong Plate. The walls were colonial ramparts – logs of *jarrah* spiked into masonry – with wings as strong as Church buttresses.

16

Once in his stride, a horse had to jump or fall. He couldn't run out. In the Maribyrnong Plate, twelve horses were jammed at the second wall. Red Hat, leading, fell this side, and threw out The Gled, and the ruck came up behind and the space between wing and wing was one struggling, screaming, kicking shambles. Four jockeys were taken out dead; three were very badly hurt, and Brunt was among the three. He told the story of the Maribyrnong Plate sometimes; and when he described how Whalley on Red Hat, said, as the mare fell under him – "God ha' mercy, I'm done for!" and how, next instant, Sithee There and White Otter had crushed the life out of poor Whalley, and the dust hid a small hell of men and horses, no one marvelled that Brunt had dropped jump-races and Australia together. Regula Baddun's owner knew that story by heart. Brunt never varied it in the telling. He had no education.

Shackles came to the Chedputter Autumn races one year, and his owner walked about insulting the sportsmen of Chedputter generally, till they went to the Honorary Secretary in a body and said, "Appoint handicappers, and arrange a race which shall break Shackles and humble the pride of his owner." The Districts rose against Shackles and sent up of their best; Ousel, who was supposed to be able to do his mile in 1-53; Petard, the stud-bred, trained by a cavalry regiment who knew how to train; Gringalet, the ewe-lamb of the 75th; Bobolink, the pride of Peshawar; and many others.

They called that race The Broken-Link Handicap, because it was to smash Shackles; and the Handicappers piled on the weights, and the Fund gave eight hundred rupees, and the distance was "round the course for all horses." Shackles' owner said, "You can arrange the race with regard to Shackles only. So long as you don't bury him under weight-cloths, I don't mind." Regula Baddun's owner said, "I throw in my mare to fret Ousel. Six furlongs is Regula's distance, and she will then lie down and die. So also will Ousel, for his jockey doesn't understand a waiting race." Now, this was a lie, Regula had been in work for two months at Dehra, and her chances were good, always supposing that Shackles broke a blood-vessel – or Brunt moved on him.

17

The plunging in the lotteries was fine. They filled eight thousand-rupee lotteries on the Broken-Link Handicap, and the account in the *Pioneer* said that "favouritism was divided." In plain English, the various contingents were wild on their respective horses; for the Handicappers had done their work well. The Honorary Secretary shouted himself hoarse through the din; and the smoke of the cheroots was like the smoke, and the rattling of the dice-boxes like the rattle of small-arm fire.

Ten horses started – very level – and Regula Baddun's owner cantered out on his hack to a place inside the circle of the course, where two bricks had been thrown. He faced towards the brick-mounds at the lower end of the course and waited.

The story of the running is in the *Pioneer*. At the end of the first mile, Shackles crept out of the ruck, well on the outside, ready to get round the turn, lay hold of the bit and spin up the straight before the others knew he had got away. Brunt was sitting still, perfectly happy, listening to the "drum-drum-drum" of the hoofs behind, and knowing that, in about twenty strides, Shackles would draw one deep breath and go. up the last half-mile like the "Flying Dutchman." As Shackles went short to take the turn and came abreast of the brick-mound, Brunt heard, above the noise of the wind in his ears, a whining, wailing voice on the offside, saying – "God ha' mercy, I'm done for!" In one stride, Brunt saw the whole seething smash of the Maribyrnong Plate before him, started in his saddle and gave a yell of terror. The start brought the heels into Shackles' side, and the scream hurt Shackles' feelings. He couldn't stop dead; but he put out his feet and slid along for fifty yards, and then, very gravely and judicially, bucked off Brunt – a shaking, terror-stricken lump, while Regula Baddun made a neck-and-neck race with Bobolink up the straight, and won by a short head – Petard a bad third. Shackles' owner, in the Stand, tried to think that his field-glasses had gone wrong. Regula Baddun's owner, waiting by the two bricks, gave one deep sigh of relief, and cantered back to the Stand. He had won, in lotteries and bets, about fifteen thousand.

It was a Broken-link Handicap with a vengeance. It broke

nearly all the men concerned, and nearly broke the heart of Shackles' owner. He went down to interview Brunt. The boy lay, livid and gasping with fright, where he had tumbled off. The sin of losing the race never seemed to strike him. All he knew was that Whalley had "called" him, that the "call" was a warning; and, were he cut in two for it, he would never get up again. His nerve had gone altogether, and he only asked his master to give him a good thrashing, and let him go. He was fit for nothing, he said. He got his dismissal, and crept up to the paddock, white as chalk, with blue lips, his knees giving way under him. People said nasty things in the paddock; but Brunt never heeded. He changed into tweeds, took his stick and went down the road, still shaking with fright, and muttering over and over again – "God ha' mercy, I'm done for!" To the best of my knowledge and belief he spoke the truth.

So now you know how the Broken-link Handicap was run and won. Of course you don't believe it. You would credit anything about Russia's designs on India, or the recommendations of the Currency Commission; but a little bit of sober fact is more than you can stand.

ICHABOD

Published in the *CMG*, 9 November 1886, with signature "Kingcraft" and subheading "(*See next column*)". Uncollected. The title means "The glory is departed". Kingcraft, whose death was reported in October, had been for years the finest pony in India. ("Full of age and honour", wrote the *Indian Planter's Gazette and Sporting News*, "the best horse of his day has been gathered to his fathers. . . .") The "next column" in the *CMG* carried an item headed "A SPORTSMAN'S LAMENT". It reported an advertisement for the Umballa Military and Hunt Meeting to be held on 16–18 December, with an assurance by the stewards, many of them officers in the Queen's Bays, that the steeplechase course had been altered and made easier: "The ditches are filled up, and all the rails removed. The fences are well sloped and bushed, and are well littered on the landing sides." A correspondent, signing himself "One of the Old School" deplores the degeneracy of the organizers: "When we wept over the departure of the 9th Lancers, it was a great consolation to us, when a keen youth said "the Bays will fill their place." He was right, and in their zeal for filling things, they have filled in the ditches on the steeple course. . . . "The course has been altered and made easier." Shades of the 9th Lancers! When we shook our lances and followed him who never returned when we crashed over boulders and mullahs into ten thousand Afghans at Shahpur, it was *not* because we had been schooled over filled-in ditches. . . ." And he invokes the support of well-known gentlemen-riders of North India in his protest. Kipling's authorship is attested by E. Kay Robinson, who tells us that the poem achieved considerable notoriety: "old steeple-chasers went humming it all over every station in upper India and swearing that it was the best thing ever written in English", while it was correspondingly resented by the Queen's Bays. ("Kipling in India", *McClure's Magazine*, vol. vii, no. 2, July 1896, pp. 105–6).

Get a nervous lady's pony – get the oldest you can find –
Strap an ulster on the pommel – tie a bedding-roll behind;
To a Hanoverian Pelham hitch a standing martingale –
Then hang upon his jaws, my son, and listen to my tale.

Many ages since, my infant, we were green as Dehra grass,
Though we lacked the shining silver we were millionaires in
     brass;
And we gathered at Umballa when the "seventies" were low,
And we rode like Helen Blazes in the days of long ago.

Those were times when life went swiftly both for rider and
     for horse –
When we sampled with our clavicles the texture of the course;
For the Stewards built the fences up to five-foot six or so,
And we "pecked" about those ramparts in the days of long
     ago.

20

Answer, man of many fractures, William Beresford – Give ear.
"Bertie", sweltering in Calcutta, Johnston, Humphreys,
    Percy Vere,
Did *you* fill these yawning ditches? Did *you* lay the railings low,
On the old Umballa race-course in the days of long ago?

Yea the ditches filled aforetime; but they filled with wrathful
    men!
Yea the railings were demolished by a bolter now and then!
More than once the "well-bushed fences" sloped before the
    staggering blow
Of a puller, gazing skyward, in the days of long ago.

There was litter – lots of litter – spread about "the landing
    side"
When a blown and basted leader checked his last half-
    hearted stride,
And the ruck came up behind him – and they made a holy
    show
On the old Umballa race-course in the days of long ago.

Many ages since, my infant, we were green as Dehra grass;
We were guileless as the morning – but we knew what riding
    was.
But a newer generation seem to make the pace more slow
Than we made it at Umballa in the days of long ago.

To an iron-bound ring-saddle nail a safety stirrup; then
Stitch a four-foot sofa-cushion just across your abdomen.
With a length of double stove-pipe guard your neck in case it
    breaks,
And – enter at Umballa, for the Military Stakes!

AT THE DISTANCE

Published in *Quartette*, 19 December 1885, with heading
" '5th Race. Ladies' Nomination. For all *bona-fide* polo ponies,

owners up. 13-2 to carry 10-7; 4 lbs. allowed for every ¼ inch under. Distance, ¾ mile on the flat. Prize, a gold locket.' – *Any Gymkhana Prospectus.*" Uncollected. The technicalities on handicapping, etc. are of the kind regularly used in advertising and reporting race-meetings in India.

Green, on Jezebel, g.c.b.m., 13-2, to himself, excitedly:

Can she stay? Here's the chestnut behind us – he's trying to pass to the right;
And I daren't pull her out from the railings! Daren't touch her! Can only sit tight,
Hands low on the withers, head forward, and watch with the tail of my eye
The chestnut's blue brow-band creep nearer. By Jove! How the beggar can fly!
He's fit to the minute – I know it, – and *Jezebel*'s not running steady.
(And I want that gold locket for Kitty) I fancy she tires already!
There's his fiddle-head up to our throat-latch. I *can't* suffer longer – Here goes!
One welt for you, close to the girth, dear! You won't shut up *now*, I suppose?
You will! Swaine and Adeney, help me! Another – and over my boot
The chestnut's red nostrils are snorting. I wish I could shake off the brute!
If *only* old Brown wasn't on him – he gives me three good on the flat –
But I'm racing for love and for Kitty, and don't care two pice for my tat.
If cat-gut and spurring can do it we're landed. Go on then you jade!
Go on, if I cut you to ribbons! No good! *Her* bolt's shot I'm afraid.
Where the deuce have we got to? – I'm blinded and dusty and sweating and done,
With a mouth like the roof of a lime-kiln – Who's shouting behind us? *I've won*!

22

Queer – Brown dying off at the finish – his chestnut's the best
  of the two –
Suppose 'twas my riding that did it – I squeezed the last
  ounce from my screw.
She's strained a back-sinew, I'm certain! Poor beast, how I've
  cut her! – Who cares?
I've won the gold locket for Kitty. Who-a up, there, you
  sweetest of mares!

  Brown, *confidentially to his mount, Robin, ch.c.b.p.*, 13-2:

I can romp in alone when I please. I can leave him behind
  when I will.
I could give him a furlong with ease; and I'm three times his
  equal in skill!
But I'm rolling about in my seat, (They'll think that I'm out o'
  my wits)
And I'm working my hands and my feet like a Cabuli dealer
  in fits.
No, Robin; you mustn't get nearer. This wasn't our form I
  admit.
When we fluttered the dovecots at Dehra, and won by two
  lengths and a bit.
I don't care a rap how it goes. *His* heart is one stake in the
  race,
(Miss Black's in the Stand, I suppose) and he'd slaughter his
  mare for a place.
I'll save the old screw all I can, though my arms are nigh
  wrenched from their socket –
Was ever a race since Gymkhanas began yet "pulled" for the
  sake of a locket?
Well, I've got a wife of my own, and I rode for her once in our
  wooing
With a man who could give me a stone, and who – did pretty
  much what I'm doing.
Come back, Rob! You're pulling like sin! (Poor tat, how he's
  making her bleed!)
Come back! – It's an eight-anna "spin", to be finished at
  twelve-anna speed.

You leather-mouthed son of a caster! I daren't pull you
more than I've done!
My faith! but we'd very near passed her – All right! Go ahead
then! He's won.
You know your own business too well, Sir? Put it all down to
wicked Miss Black!
I ran you to lose. Don't you tell, Sir! *He's* ruined a second-rate
hack.

CHAPTER HEADINGS

Ride with an idle whip, ride with an unused heel,
But, once in a way, there will come a day
When the colt must be taught to feel
The lash that falls, and the curb that galls, and the sting of
the rowelled steel.

"Stopped in the straight when the race was his own –
Look at him cutting it – cur to the bone!"
Ask ere the youngster be rated and chidden
What did he carry and how was he ridden?
Maybe they used him too much at the start.
Maybe fate's weight-cloths are breaking his heart.

3

A WALKING DELEGATE

This is the first story in the Kipling canon in which he made animals talk, in this case horses. This device was, of course, followed with immense success in *The Maltese Cat*, *The Jungle Books* and other stories.

For modern readers it is probably necessary to explain something of the story's provenance. It is set in Vermont between the years 1892 to 1986, when Kipling was living there, after his marriage to Carrie Balestier, a period which began happily enough with the birth of his beloved daughter Josephine after whose death a few short years later, his second daughter was to write that "a light had gone out which could never be rekindled." Sadly those years were to end in bitterness and recrimination after a row with Carrie's ne'er-do-well brother, Beatty Balestier.

The "Walking delegate", of the title was Vermontese for a union organiser and propagandist who went amongst the workers preaching solidarity, and who was to Kipling's mind a trouble-maker and rabble-rouser. Here he has identified him as the yellow horse who comes to the other horses at grass in Kipling's meadow to try and organise them to cause agitation against their master. In it Kipling has caught the various Vermont dialects with an exactitude he did not always display in rendering the argot of other nationalities, notably Mulvaney's "stage Irish" which is like nothing on earth. The yellow horse duly gets his comeuppance in Kipling's terms but, for horsemen at least, there is more to the story than that.

Carrie according to her Vermont neighbours was inclined

25

to put on airs and had grandiose ideas of her position as the wife of a famous and best-selling author. Kipling bought her two carriage horses, whom he named "Rod" and "Ric", and these she drove around Battleboro in some style with a top-hatted coachman on the box. One winter she was ill and they proved too much for her. Kipling replaced them with two thoroughbreds whom he called "Nip" and "Tuck" and which he bought from Beatty Balestier for $650 a sum which we are told kept the spendthrift and rapscallion Beatty solvent for only a few months. Thus Kipling had cause to reflect on the truth and accuracy of those verses from *Hafiz* which I have already quoted. "Rod" and "Ric" and "Nip" and "Tuck" figure in the story under their own names but, and far more importantly, writing the story gave Kipling the idea for the unforgettable *The Maltese Cat* which he wrote only a few months after he had finished *A Walking Delegate*.

A WALKING DELEGATE

According to the custom of Vermont, Sunday afternoon is salting-time on the farm, and, unless something very important happens, we attend to the salting ourselves. Dave and Peter, the red oxen, are treated first; they stay in the home meadow, ready for work on Monday. Then come the cows, with Pan, the calf, who should have been turned into veal long ago, but survived on account of his manners; and, lastly, the horses, scattered through the seventy acres of the Back Pasture.

You must go down by the brook that feeds the clicking, bubbling water-ram; up through the sugar-bush, where the young maple undergrowth closes round you like a shallow sea; next follow the faint line of an old county-road running past two green hollows fringed with wild rose that mark the cellars of two ruined houses; then by Lost Orchard, where nobody ever comes except in cider-time; then across another brook, and so into the Back Pasture. Half of it is pine and hemlock and spruce, with sumach and little juniper-bushes, and the other half is grey rock and boulder and moss, with green streaks of brake and swamp; but the horses like it well enough – our own, and the others that are turned down there to feed at fifty cents a week. Most people walk to the Back Pasture, and find it very rough work; but one can get there in a buggy, if the horse knows what is expected of him. The safest conveyance is our coupé. This began life as a buckboard, and we bought it for five dollars from a sorrowful man who had no other sort of possessions; and the seat came off one night when we were turning a corner in a hurry. After that alteration it made a beautiful salting-machine, if you held tight, because there was nothing to catch your feet when you fell out, and the slats rattled tunes.

One Sunday afternoon we went out with the salt as usual. It was a broiling hot day, and we could not find the horses anywhere till we let Tedda Babler, the bob-tailed mare who throws up the dirt with her big hoofs exactly as a tedder throws hay, have her head. Clever as she is, she tipped the coupé over in a hidden brook before she came out on a ledge of rock where all the horses had gathered and were switching flies. The Deacon was the first to call to her. He is a very dark iron-grey four-year-old, son of Grandee. He has been handled since he was two, was driven in a light cart before he was three, and now ranks as an absolutely steady lady's horse – proof against steam rollers, grade-crossings, and street processions.

"Salt!" said the Deacon, joyfully. "You're dreffle late, Tedda."

"Any – any place to cramp the coupé?" Tedda panted. "It draws turr'ble this weather. I'd 'a' come sooner, but they didn't know what they wanted – ner haow. Fell out twice, both of them. I don't understand sech foolishness."

"You look consider'ble het up. Guess you'd better cramp her under them pines, an' cool off a piece."

Tedda scrambled on the ledge, and cramped the coupé in the shade of a tiny little wood of pines, while my companion and I lay down among the brown, silky needles, and gasped. All the home horses were gathered round us, enjoying their Sunday leisure.

27

There were Rod and Rick, the seniors on the farm. They were the regular road-pair, bay with black points, full brothers, aged, sons of a Hambletonian sire and a Morgan dam. There were Nip and Tuck, seal-browns, rising six, brother and sister, Black Hawks by birth, perfectly matched, just finishing their education, and as handsome a pair as man could wish to find in a forty-mile drive. There was Muldoon, our ex-car-horse, bought at a venture, and any colour you choose that is not white; and Tweezy, who comes from Kentucky, with an affliction of his left hip, which makes him a little uncertain how his hind legs are moving. He and Muldoon had been hauling gravel all the week for our new road. The Deacon you know already. Last of all, and eating something, was our faithful Marcus Aurelius Antoninus, the black buggy-horse, who had seen us through every state of weather and road, the horse who was always standing in harness before some door or other – a philosopher with the appetite of a shark and the manners of an archbishop. Tedda Gabler was a new "trade," with a reputation for vice which was really the result of bad driving. She had one working gait, which she could hold till further notice; a Roman nose; a large, prominent eye; a shaving-brush of a tail; and an irritable temper. She took her salt through her bridle; but the others trotted up nuzzling and wickering for theirs, till we emptied it on the clean rocks. They were all standing at ease, on three legs for the most part, talking the ordinary gossip of the Back Pasture – about the scarcity of water, and gaps in the fence, and how the early windfalls tasted that season – when little Rick blew the last few grains of his allowance into a crevice, and said:

"Hurry, boys! Might ha' knowed that livery-plug would be around."

We heard a clatter of hoofs, and there climbed up from the ravine below a fifty-center transient – a wall-eyed, yellow frame-house of a horse, sent up to board from a livery-stable in town, where they called him "The Lamb," and never let him out except at night and to strangers. My companion, who knew and had broken most of the horses, looked at the ragged hammer-head as it rose, and said quietly:

"Nice beast. Man-eater, if he gets the chance – see his eye. Kicker, too – see his hocks. Western horse."

The animal lumbered up, snuffling and grunting. His feet showed that he had not worked for weeks and weeks, and our creatures drew together significantly.

"As usual," he said, with an underhung sneer – "bowin'" your heads before the Oppressor, that comes to spend his leisure gloatin' over you."

"Mine's done," said the Deacon; he licked up the remnant of his salt, dropped his nose in his master's hand, and sang a little grace all to himself. The Deacon has the most enchanting manners of any one I know.

"An' fawnin' on them for what is your inalienable right. It's humiliatin'," said the yellow horse, sniffing to see if he could find a few spare grains.

"Go daown hill, then, Boney," the Deacon replied. "Guess you'll find somefin' to eat still, if yer hain't hogged it all. You've ett more'n any three of us to-day – an' day 'fore that – an' the last two months – sence you've been here.'

"I am not addressin' myself to the young an' immature. I am speakin' to those whose opinion *an'* experience commands respect."

I saw Rod raise his head as though he were about to make a remark; then he dropped it again, and stood three-cornered, like a plough-horse. Rod can cover his mile in a shade under three minutes on an ordinary road to an ordinary buggy. He is tremendously powerful behind, but, like most Hambletonians, he grows a trifle sullen as he gets older. No one can love Rod very much; but no one can help respecting him.

"I wish to wake *those*," the yellow horse went on, "to an abidin' sense o' their wrongs an' their injuries an' their outrages."

'Haow's that?" said Marcus Aurelius Antoninus, dreamily. He thought Boney was talking of some kind of feed.

"An' when I say outrages and injuries" – Boney waved his tail furiously – "I mean 'em, too. Great Oats! That's just what I *do* mean, plain an' straight."

"The gentleman talks quite earnest," said Tuck, the mare,

to Nip, her brother. "There's no doubt thinkin' broadens the horizons o' the mind. His language is right lofty."

"Hesh, sis," Nip answered. "He hain't widened nothin' 'cep' the circle he's ett in pasture. They feed words fer beddin' where he comes from."

"It's elegant talkin', though," Tuck returned, with an unconvinced toss of her pretty, lean, little head.

The yellow horse heard her, and struck an attitude which he meant to be extremely impressive. It made him look as though he had been badly stuffed.

"Now I ask you – I ask you without prejudice an' without favour – what has Man the Oppressor ever done for you? Are you not inalienably entitled to the free air o' heaven, blowin' acrost this boundless prairie?"

'Hev ye ever wintered here?" said the Deacon, merrily, while the others snickered. "It's kinder cool."

"Not yet," said Boney. "I come from the boundless confines o' Kansas, where the noblest of our kind have their abidin'-place among the sunflowers on the threshold o' the settin' sun in his glory."

"An' they sent you ahead as a sample?" said Rick, with an amused quiver of his long, beautifully-groomed tail, as thick and as fine and as wavy as a quadroon's back hair.

"Kansas, sir, needs no adver*tise*ment. Her native sons rely on themselves an' their native sires. Yes, sir."

Then Tweezy lifted up his wise and polite old face. His affliction makes him bashful as a rule, but he is ever the most courteous of horses.

"Excuse me, suh," he said slowly, "but, unless I have been misinfohmed, most of your prominent siahs, suh, are impoted from Kentucky; an' *I'm* from Paduky."

There was the least little touch of pride in the last words.

"Any horse dat knows beans," said Muldoon, suddenly (he had been standing with his hairy chin on Tweezy's broad quarters), "gets outer Kansas 'fore dey crip his shoes. I blew in dere frum Ioway in de days o' me youth an' innocence, and I wuz grateful when dey boxed me fer N'York. You can't tell *me* anything about Kansas I don't wanter fergit. De Belt

Line stables ain't no Hoffman House, but dey're Vanderbilt's 'longside o' Kansas."

"What the horses o' Kansas think to-day, the horses of America will think to-morrow; an' I tell *you* that when the horses of America rise in their might, the day o' the Oppressor is ended."

There was a pause, till Rick said, with a little grunt:

"Ef you put it that way, every one of us has riz in his might, 'cep' Marcus, maybe. Marky, 'j ever rise in yer might?"

"Nope," said Marcus Aurelius Antoninus, thoughtfully quidding over a mouthful of grass. "I seen a heap o' fools try, though."

"You admit that you riz?" said the Kansas horse, excitedly. "Then why – why in Kansas did you ever go under again?"

"Horse can't walk on his hind legs *all* the time," said the Deacon.

"Not when he's jerked over on his back 'fore he knows what fetched him. We've all done it, Boney," said Rick. "Nip an' Tuck, they tried it, spite o' what the Deacon told 'em; and the Deacon, he tried it, spite o' what me an' Rod told him; an' me an' Rod tried it, spite o' what Grandee told us; an' I guess Grandee he tried it, spite o' what his dam told him. It's the same old circus from generation to generation. 'Colt can't see why he's called on to back. Same old rearin' on end – straight up. Same old feelin' that you've bested 'em this time. Same old little yank at yer mouth when you're up good an' tall. Same old Pegasus-act, wonderin' where you'll 'light. Same old whop when you hit the dirt with your head where your tail should be, and your in'ards shook up like a bran-mash. Same old voice in your ear, 'Waal, ye little fool, an' what did you reckon to make by that?' We're through with risin' in our might on this farm. We go to pole er single, accordin' ez we're hitched."

'An' Man the Oppressor sets an' gloats over you, same as he's settin' now. Hain't that been your experience, madam?"

This last remark was addressed to Tedda, and any one could see with half an eye that poor, old, anxious, fidgety Tedda, stamping at the flies, must have left a wild and tumultuous youth behind her.

31

"'Pends on the man," she answered, shifting from one foot to the other, and addressing herself to the home horses. "They abused me dreffle when I was young. I guess I was sperrity an' nervous some, but they didn't allow for that. 'Twas in Monroe County, Noo York, an' sence then till I come here, I've run away with more men than 'ud fill a boardin'-house. Why, the man that sold me here he says to the boss, s' he: 'Mind, now, I've warned you. 'Twon't be none of my fault if she sheds you daown the road. Don't you drive her in a top-buggy, ner 'thout winkers,' s' he, 'ner 'thout this bit, ef you look to come home behind her.' 'N' the fust thing the boss did was to git the top-buggy."

"Can't say as I like top-buggies," said Rick; "they don't balance good."

"'Suit me to a harr," said Marcus Aurelius Antoninus. "Top-buggy means the baby's in behind, an' I kin stop while she gathers the pretty flowers – yes, an' pick a maouthful, too. The women-folk all say I hev to be humoured, an' – I don't kerry things to the sweatin'-point."

"'Course I've no prejudice against a top-buggy s' long's I can see it," Tedda went on quickly. "It's ha'f-seein' the pesky thing bobbin' an balancin' behind the winkers gets on *my* nerves. Then the boss looked at the bit they'd sold with me, an' s' he: 'Jimmy Christmas! This 'ud make a clothes-horse stan' 'n end!' Then he gave me a plain bar bit, an' fitted it 's if there was some feelin' to my maouth."

"Hain't ye got any, Miss Tedda?" said Tuck, who has a mouth like velvet, and knows it.

"Might 'a' had, Miss Tuck, but I've forgot. Then he give me an open bridle, – my style's an open bridle – an' – I dunnos as I ought to tell this by rights – he give – me – a kiss."

"My!" said Tuck, "I can't tell fer the shoes o' me what makes some men so fresh."

"Pshaw, sis," said Nip, "what the sense in actin' so? *You* git a kiss reg'lar's hitchin'-up time."

"Well, you needn't tell, smarty," said Tuck, with a squeal and a kick.

"I'd heard o' kisses, o' course," Tedda went on, "but they hadn't come my way specially. I don't mind tellin' I was that took aback at that man's doin's he might ha' lit fire-crackers on my saddle. Then we went out jest's if a kiss was nothin,'' an' I wasn't three strides into my gait 'fore I felt the boss knoo his business, an' was trustin' me. So I studied to please him, an' he never took the whip from the dash – a whip drives me plump distracted – an' the upshot was that – waal, I've come up the Back Pasture to-day, an' the coupé's tipped clear over twice, an' I've waited till 'twuz fixed each time. You kin judge for yourselves. I don't set up to be no better than my neighbours, – specially with my tail snipped off the way 'tis, – but I want you all to know Tedda's quit fightin' in harness, or out of it, 'cep' when there's a born fool in the pasture, stuffin' his stummick with board that ain't rightly hisn, 'cause he hain't earned it.''

"Meanin' me, madam?'' said the yellow horse.

"Ef the shoe fits, clinch it,'' said Tedda, snorting. "*I* named no names, though, to be sure, some folks are mean enough an' greedy enough to do 'thout 'em.''

"There's a deal to be forgiven to ignorance,'' said the yellow horse, with an ugly look in his blue eye.

"Seemin'ly, yes; or some folks 'ud ha' been kicked raound the pasture 'bout onct a minute sence they came – board er no board.''

"But what you do *not* understand, if you will excuse me, madam, is that the whole principle o' servitood, which includes keep an' feed, starts from a radically false basis; an' I am proud to say that me an' the majority o' the horses o' Kansas think the entire concern should be relegated to the limbo of exploded superstitions. I say we're too progressive for that. I say we're too enlightened for that. 'Twas good enough's long's we didn't think, but naow – but naow – a new loominary has arisen on the horizon!''

"Meanin' you?'' said the Deacon.

"The horses o' Kansas are behind me with their multitoodinous thunderin' hoofs, an' we say, simply but grandly, that we take our stand with all four feet on the inalienable rights of the horse, pure and simple, – the high-toned child o' nature, fed by the same wavin' grass, cooled by the same ripplin' brook, – yes, an' warmed by the same gen'rous sun as

33

falls impartially on the outside an' the *inside* of the pampered machine o' the trottin'-track, or the bloated coupé-horses o' these yere Eastern cities. Are we not the same flesh and blood?"

"Not by a bushel an' a half," said the Deacon, under his breath. "Grandee never was in Kansas."

"My! Ain't that elegant, though, abaout the wavin' grass an' the ripplin' brooks?" Tuck whispered in Nip's ear. "The gentleman's real convincin',' *I* think."

"I say we *are* the same flesh an' blood! Are we to be separated, horse from horse, by the artificial barriers of a trottin'record, or are we to look down upon each other on the strength o' the gifts o' nature – an extry inch below the knee, or slightly more powerful quarters? What's the use o' them advantages to you? Man the Oppressor comes along, an' sees you're likely an' good-lookin', an' grinds you to the face o' the earth. What for? For his own pleasure: for his own convenience! Young an' old, black an' bay, white an' grey, there's no distinctions made between us. We're ground up together under the remorseless teeth o' the engines of oppression!"

"Guess his brichin' must ha' broke goin' daown-hill," said the Deacon. "Slippery road, maybe, an' the buggy come onter him, an' he didn't know 'nough to hold back. That don't feel like teeth, though. Maybe he busted a shaft, an' it pricked him."

"An' I come to you from Kansas, wavin' the tail o' friendship to all an' sundry, an' in the name of the uncounted millions o' pure-minded high-toned horses now strugglin' toward the light o' freedom, I say to you, rub noses with us in our sacred an' holy cause. The power is yourn. Without you, I say, Man the Oppressor cannot move himself from place to place. Without you he cannot reap, he cannot sow, he cannot plough."

"Mighty odd place, Kansas!" said Marcus Aurelius Antoninus. "Seemin'ly they reap in the spring an' plough in the fall. 'Guess it's right fer them, but 'twould make me kinder giddy."

"The produc's of your untirin' industry would rot on the

ground if you did not weakly consent to help them. *Let* 'em rot, I say! Let him call you to the stables in vain an' nevermore! Let him shake his ensnarin' oats under your nose in vain! Let the Brahmas roost in the buggy, an' the rats run riot round the reaper! Let him walk on his two hind feet till they blame well drop off! With no more soul-destroyin' races for his pleasure! Then, an' not till then, will Man the Oppressor know where he's at. Quit workin', fellow-sufferers an' slaves! Kick! Rear! Plunge." Lie down on the shafts, an' woller! Smash an' destroy! The conflict will be but short, an' the victory is certain. After that we can press our inalienable rights to eight quarts o' oats a day, two good blankets, an' a fly-net an' the best o' stablin'.' "

The yellow horse shut his yellow teeth with a triumphant snap; and Tuck said, with a sigh: "Seems' 's if somethin' ought to be done. Don't seem right, somehow – oppressin' us an' all, – to my way o' thinkin'."

Said Muldoon, in a far-away and sleepy voice: "Who in Vermont's goin' to haul de inalienable oats? Dey weigh like Sam Hill, an' sixty bushel at dat allowance ain't goin' to last t'ree weeks here. An' dere's de winter hay for five mont's!"

"We can settle those minor details when the great cause is won," said the yellow horse. "Let us return simply but grandly to our inalienable rights – the right o' freedom on these yere verdant hills, an' no invijjus distinctions o' track an' pedigree."

"What in stables 'jer call an invijjus distinction?" said the Deacon, stiffly.

"Fer one thing, bein' a bloated, pampered trotter jest because you happen to be raised that way, an' couldn't no more help trottin' then eatin'."

"Do ye know anythin' about trotters?" said the Deacon.

"I've seen 'em trot. That was enough for me. *I* don't want to know any more. Trottin' 's immoral."

"Waal, I'll tell you this much. They don't bloat, an' they don't pamp – much. I don't hold out to be no trotter myself, though I am free to say I had hopes that way – oncet. But I *do* say, fer I've seen 'em trained, that a trotter don't trot with his feet; he trots with his head; an' he does more work – ef you know what *that* is – in a week than you er your sire ever done in all your lives. He's everlastingly at it, a trotter is; an' when he isn't, he's studyin' haow. You seen 'em trot? Much you hev! You was hitched to a rail, back o' the stand, in a buck-board with a soap-box nailed on the slats, an' a frowzy buff'lo atop, while your man peddled rum for lemonade to little boys as thought they was actin' manly, till you was both run off the track and jailed – you intoed, shufflin', sway-backed, wind-suckin' skate, you!'

"Don't get het up, Deacon," said Tweezy, quietly. "Now, suh, would you consider a foxtrot, an' single-foot, an' rack, an' pace, *an'* amble, distinctions not worth distinguishin'? I assuah you, gentlemen, there was a time befo' I was afflicted in my hip, if you'll pardon me, Miss Tuck, when I was quite celebrated in Paduky for *all* those gaits; an' in my opinion the Deacon's co'rect when he says that a ho'se of any position in society gets his gaits by his haid, an' not by – his, ah, limbs, Miss Tuck. I reckon I'm very little good now, but I'm re-memberin' the things I used to do befo' I took to transpo'tin' real estate with the help and assistance of this gentleman here." He looked at Muldoon.

"Invijjus arterficial hind-legs!" said the ex-carhorse, with a grunt of contempt. "On de Belt Line we don't reckon no horse wuth his keep 'less he kin switch de car off de track, run her round on de cobbles, an' dump her in ag'in ahead o' de truck what's blockin' him. Dere is a way o' swinging yer quarters when de drivers say. 'Yank her out, boys!' dat takes a year to learn. Onct yer git onter it, youse kin yank a cable-car outer a manhole. I don't advertise myself fer no circus-horse, but I knew dat trick better than most, an' dey was good to me in de stables, fer I saved time on de Belt – an' time's what dey hunt in N' York.'

"But the simple child o' nature – 'the yellow horse began.

"Oh, go an' unscrew her splints! You're talkin' through yer bandages," said Muldoon, with a horse-laugh. "Dere ain't no loose-box for de simple child o' nature on de Belt Line, wid de *Paris* comin' in an' de *Teutonic* goin' out, an' de trucks an' de coupés sayin' things, an' de heavy freight movin' down fer de Boston boat 'bout t'ree o'clock of an August afternoon, in de middle of a hot wave when de fat Kanucks an' Western horses drops dead on de block. De simple child o' nature had better chase himself inter de water. Every man at de end of his lines is mad or loaded or silly, an' de cop's madder an' loadeder an' sillier dan de rest. Dey all take it outer de horses. Dere's no wavin' brooks ner ripplin' grass on de Belt Line. Run her out on de cobbles wid de sparks flyin', an' stop when de cop slugs you on de bone o' yer nose. Dat's N' York; see?"

"I was always told s'ciety in Noo York was dreffle refined an' high-toned," said Tuck. 'We're lookin' to go there one o' these days, Nip an' me."

"Oh, *you* won't see no Belt business where you'll go miss. De man dat wants you'll want you bad, an' he'll summer you on Long Island er at Newport, wid a winky-pinky silver harness an' an English coachman. You'll make a star-hitch, you an' yer brother, miss. But I guess you won't have no nice smooth bar bit. Dey checks 'em, an' dey bangs deir tails, an' dey bits 'em, de city folk, an' dey says it's English, ye know, and dey darsen't cut a horse loose 'ca'se o' de cops. N' York's no place fer a horse, 'less he's on de Belt, an' can go round wid de boys. Wisht *I* was in de Fire Department!"

"But did you never stop to consider the degradin' servitood of it all:" said the yellow horse.

"You don't stop on de Belt, cully. You're stopped. An' we was all in de servitood business, man an' horse, an' Jimmy dat sold de papers. Guess de passengers weren't out to grass neither, by de way dey acted. I done my turn, an' I'm none o' Barnum's crowd; but any horse dat's worked on de Belt four years don't train wid no simple child o' nature – not by de whole length o' N' York."

"But can it be possible that with your experience, and at your time of life, you do not believe that all horses are free and equal?" said the yellow horse.

"Not till dey're dead," Muldoon answered quietly. "An' den it depends on de gross total o' buttons an' mucilage dey gits outer youse at Barren Island."

"They tell me you're a prominent philosopher." The

37

yellow horse turned to Marcus. "Can *you* deny a basic and pivotal statement such as this?"

"I don't deny anything'," said Marcus Aurelius Antoninus, cautiously; "but ef you *ast* me, I should say 'twuz more different sorts o' clipped oats of a lie than anythin' I've had my teeth into sence I wuz foaled."

"Are you a horse?" said the yellow horse.

"Them that knows me best 'low I am."

"Ain't *I* a horse?"

"Yep; one kind of."

"Then ain't you an' me equal?"

"How fer kin you go in a day to a loaded buggy, drawin' five hundred pounds?" Marcus asked carelessly.

"That has nothing to do with the case," the yellow horse answered excitedly.

"There's nothing I know hez more to do with the case," Marcus replied.

"Kin ye yank a full car outer de tracks ten times in de mornin'?" said Muldoon.

"Kin ye go to Keene – forty-two mile in an afternoon – with a mate," said Rick, "an' turn out bright an' early next mornin'?"

"Was there evah any time in your careah, such – I am not referrin' to the present circumstances, but our mutual glorious past – when you could carry a pretty girl to market hahnsome, an' let her knit all the way on account o' the smoothness o' the motion?" said Tweezy.

"Kin you keep your feet through the West River Bridge, with the narrer-gage comin' in on one side, an' the Montreal flyer the other, an' the old bridge teeterin' between?" said the Deacon. "Kin you put your nose down on the cowcatcher of a locomotive when you're waitin' at the depôt an' let 'em play 'Curfew shall not ring to-night,' with the big brass bell?"

"Kin you hold back when the brichin' breaks? Kin you stop fer orders when your nigh hind leg's over your trace an' ye feel good of a frosty mornin'?" said Nip, who had only heard that trick last winter, and thought it was the crown of horsely knowledge.

"What's the use o' talkin'?" said Tedda Gabler, scornfully. "What kin ye do?"

"I rely on my simple rights – the inalienable rights o' my unfettered horsehood. An' I am proud to say I have never, since my first shoes, lowered myself to obeyin' the will o' man."

"Must ha' had a heap o' whips broke over yer yaller back," said Tedda. "Hev ye found it paid any?"

"Sorrer has been my portion since the day I was foaled. Blows an' boots an' whips an' insults – injury, outrage, an' oppression. I would not endoor the degradin' badges o' servitood that connect us with the buggy an' the farm-wagon."

"It's amazin' difficult to draw a buggy 'thout traces er collar er breast-strap er somefin'," said Marcus. "A Power-machine for sawin' wood is 'most the only thing there's no straps to. I've helped saw's much as three cord in an afternoon in a Power-machine. Slep', too, most o' the time, I did; but 'tain't half as interestin' ez goin' daown-taown in the Concord."

"Concord don't hender *you* goin' to sleep any," said Nip. "My throat-lash! D' you remember when you lay down in the sharves last week, waitin' at the piazza?"

"Pshaw! That didn't hurt the sharves. They wuz good an' wide, an' I lay down keerful. The folks kep' me hitched up nigh an hour 'fore they started; an' larfed – why, they all but lay down themselves with larfin'. Say, Boney, if you've got to be hitched *to* anything that goes on wheels, you've got to be hitched *with* somefin'."

"Go an' jine a circus," said Muldoon, "an' walk on your hind legs. All de horses dat knows too much to work [he pronounced it 'woik,' New York fashion] jine de circus."

"I am not sayin' anythin' again' work," said the yellow horse; "work is the finest thing in the world."

"Seems too fine fer some of us," Teddy snorted.

"I only ask that each horse should work for himself, an' enjoy the profit of his labours. Let him work intelligently, an' not as a machine."

"There ain't no horse that works like a machine," Marcus began.

"There's no way o' workin' that doesn't mean goin' to pole

or single – they never put me in the Power-machine – er under saddle," said Rick.

"Oh, shucks! We're talkin' same ez we graze," said Nip, "raound an' raound in circles. Rod, we hain't heard from you yet, an' you've more knowhow than any span here."

Rod, the off-horse of the pair, had been standing with one hip lifted, like a tired cow; and you could only tell by the quick flutter of the haw across his eye, from time to time, that he was paying any attention to the argument. He thrust his jaw out sidewise, as his habit is when he pulls, and changed his leg. His voice was hard and heavy, and his ears were close to his big, plain Hambletonian head.

"How old are you?" he said to the yellow horse.

"Nigh thirteen, I guess."

"Mean age; ugly age; I'm gettin' that way myself. How long hev ye been pawin' this fire-fanged stable litter?"

"If you mean my principles, I've held 'em sence I was three."

"Mean age; ugly age; teeth give heaps o' trouble then. Set a colt to actin' crazy fer a while. *You*'ve kep' it up, seemin'ly. D'ye talk much to your neighbours fer a steady thing?"

"I uphold the principles o' the Cause wherever I am pastured."

"Done a heap o' good, I guess?"

"I am proud to say I have taught a few of my companions the principles o' freedom an' liberty."

"Meaning' they ran away er kicked when they got the chanst?"

"I was talkin' in the abstrac', an' not in the concrete. My teachin's educated them."

"What a horse, specially a young horse, hears in the abstrac', he's liable to do in the Concord. You wuz handled late, I presoom."

Four, risin' five."

"That's where the trouble began. Driv' by a woman, like ez not – eh?"

"Not fer long," said the yellow horse, with a snap of his teeth.

"Spilled her?"

"I heerd she never drove again."

40

"Any children?"

"Buckboards full of 'em."

"Men too?"

"I have shed conside'ble men in my time."

"By kickin'?"

"Any way that come along. Fallin' back over the dash is as handy as most."

"They must be turr'ble afraid o' you daown-taown?"

"They've sent me here to get rid o' me. I guess they spend their time talkin' over my campaigns."

"*I* wanter know!"

"Yes, *sir*. Now, all you gentlemen have asked me what I can do. I'll just show you. See them two fellers lyin' down by the buggy?"

"Yep; one of 'em owns me. T'other broke me," said Rod.

"Get 'em out here in the open, an' I'll show you something. Lemme hide back o'you peoples, so's they won't see what I'm at."

"Meanin' ter kill 'em?" Rod drawled. There was a shudder of horror through the others; but the yellow horse never noticed.

"I'll catch 'em by the back o' the neck, an pile-drive 'em a piece. They can suit 'emselves about livin' when I'm through with 'em."

"Shouldn't wonder ef they did," said Rod.

The yellow horse had hidden himself very cleverly behind the others as they stood in a group, and was swaying his head close to the ground with a curious scythe-like motion, looking sideways out of his wicked eyes. You can never mistake a man-eater getting ready to knock a man down. We had had one to pasture the year before.

"See that?" said my companion, turning over on the pine-needles. "Nice for a woman walking 'cross lots, wouldn't it be?"

"Bring 'em out!" said the yellow horse, hunching his sharp back. "There's no chance among them tall trees. Bring out the – oh! Ouch!"

It was a right-and-left kick from Muldoon. I had no idea that the old car-horse could lift so quickly. Both blows caught

41

the yellow horse full and fair in the ribs, and knocked the breath out of him.

"What's that for?" he said angrily, when he recovered himself; but I noticed he did not draw any nearer to Muldoon than was necessary.

Muldoon never answered, but discoursed to himself in the whining grunt that he uses when he is going down-hill in front of a heavy load. We call it singing; but I think it's something much worse, really. The yellow horse blustered and squealed a little, and at last said that, if it was a horse-fly that had stung Muldoon, he would accept an apology.

"You'll get it," said Muldoon, "in de sweet by-and-by – all de apology you've any use for. Excuse me interruptin' you, Mr. Rod, but I'm like Tweezy – I've a Southern drawback in me hind legs."

'Naow, I want you all here to take notice, and you'll learn something," Rod went on. "This yaller-backed skate comes to our pastur' –"

'Not havin' paid his board," put in Tedda.

"Not havin' earned his board, an' talks smooth to us abaout ripplin' brooks an' waving' grass, an' his high-toned, pure-souled horsehood, which don't hender him sheddin' women an' childern, an' fallin' over the dash onter men. You heard his talk, an' you thought it mighty fine, some o' you."

Tuck looked guilty here, but she did not say anything.

"Bit by bit he goes on ez you have heard."

"I was talkin' in the abstrac'," said the yellow horse, in an altered voice.

"Abstrac' be switched! Ez I've said, it's this yer blamed abstrac' business that makes the young uns cut up in the Concord; an' abstrac' or no abstrac', he crep' on an' on till he comes to killin' plain an' straight – killin' them as never done him no harm, jest beca'se they owned horses."

"An' knowed how to manage 'em," said Tedda. "That makes it worse."

"Waal, he didn't kill 'em, anyway," said Marcus. "He'd ha' been half killed ef he had tried."

"Makes no differ," Rod answered. "He meant to; an' ef he

hadn't – s'pose we want the Back Pasture turned into a biffin'-ground on our only day er rest? 'S'pose *we* want *our* men walkin' round with bits er lead pipe an' a twitch, an' their hands full o' stones to throw at us, same's if we wuz hogs er hooky keows? More'n that, leavin' out Tedda here – an' I guess it's more her maouth than her manners stands in her light – there ain't a horse on this farm that ain't a woman's horse, an' proud of it. An' this yer bog-spavined Kansas sunflower goes up an' daown the length o' the country, traded off and traded on, boastin' ez he's shed women – an' childern. I don't say ez a woman in a buggy ain't a fool. I don't say ez she ain't the lastin'est kind er fool, ner I don't say a child ain't worse – spattin' the lines an' standin' up an' hollerin' – but I *do* say, 'tain't none of our business to shed 'em daown the road."

"We don't," said the Deacon. "The baby tried to git some o' my tail for a sooveneer last fall when I was up to the haouse, an' I didn't kick. Boney's talk ain't goin' to hurt us any. We ain't colts."

"Thet's what you *think*. Bimeby you git into a tight corner, 'Lection day er Valley Fair, like's not, daown-taown, when you're all het an' lathery, an' pestered with flies, an' thirsty, an' sick o' bein' worked in an' aout 'tween buggies. *Then* somethin' whispers inside o' yer winkers, bringin' up all that talk abaout servitood an' inalienable truck an' sech like, an' jest then a Militia gun goes off, er your wheels hit, an' – waal, you're only another horse ez can't be trusted. I've been there time an' again. Boys – fer I've seen you all bought er broke – on my solemn repitation fer a three-minute clip, I ain't givin' you no bran-mash o' my own fixin'. I'm tellin' you my experiences, an' I've had ez heavy a load an' ez high a check's any horse here. I wuz born with a splint on my near fore ez big's a walnut, an' the cussed, three-cornered Hambletonian temper that sours up an' curdles daown ez you git older. I've favoured my splint; even little Rick he don't know what it's cost me to keep my end up sometimes; an' I've fit my temper in stall an' harness, hitched up an' at pasture till the sweat trickled off my hoofs, an' they thought I wuz off condition, an' drenched me."

"When my affliction came," said Tweezy, gently, "I was very near to losin' my manners. Allow me to extend to you my sympathy, suh."

Rick said nothing, but he looked at Rod curiously. Rick is a sunny-tempered child who never bears malice, and I don't think he quite understood. He gets his temper from his mother, as a horse should.

"I've been there too, Rod," said Tedda. "Open confession's good for the soul, an' all Monroe County knows I've had my experiences."

"But if you will excuse me, suh, that pusson' – Tweezy looked unspeakable things at the yellow horse – "that pusson who has insulted our intelligences comes from Kansas. An' what a ho'se of his position, an' Kansas at that, says cannot, by any stretch of the halter, concern gentlemen of *our* position. There's no shadow of equal'ty, suh, not even for one kick. He's beneath our contempt."

"Let him talk," said Marcus. "It's always inte*re*stin' to know what another horse thinks. It don't tech us."

"An' he talks so, too," said Tuck. "I've never heard anythin' so smart for a long time."

Again Rod stuck out his jaws sidewise, and went on slowly, as though he were slugging on a plain bit at the end of a thirty-mile drive:

"I want all you here ter understand that ther' ain't no Kansas, ner no Kentucky, ner yet no Vermont, in *our* business. There's jest two kind o' horse in the United States – them ez can an' will do their work after bein' properly broke an' handled, an' them ez won't. I'm sick an' tired o' this everlastin' tail-switchin' an' wickerin' abaout one State er another. A horse kin be proud o' his State, an' swap lies abaout it in stall or when he's hitched to a block, ef he keers to put in fly-time that way; but he hain't no right to let that pride o' hisn interfere with his work, ner to make it an excuse fer claimin' he's different. That's colt's talk, an' don't you fergit it, Tweezy. An', Marcus, you remember that bein' a philosopher, an' anxious to save trouble, – fer you *are* – don't excuse you from jumpin' with all your feet on a slack-jawed, crazy clay-bank like Boney here. It's leavin' 'em alone that

44

gives 'em their chance to ruin colts an' kill folks. An', Tuck, waal, you're a mare anyways – but when a horse comes along an' covers up all his talk o' killin' with ripplin' brooks, an' wavin' grass, an' eight quarts of oats a day free, *after* killin' his man, don't you be run away with by his yap. You're too young an' too nervous."

"I'll – I'll have nervous prostration sure ef there's a fight here," said Tuck, who saw what was in Rod's eye; "I'm – I'm that sympathetic I'd run away clear to next caounty."

"Yep; I know that kind o' sympathy. Jest lasts long enough to start a fuss, an' then lights aout to make new trouble. I hain't been ten years in harness fer nuthin'. Naow, we're goin' to keep school with Boney fer a spell."

"Say, look a-here, you ain't goin' to hurt me, are you? Remember, I belong to a man in town," cried the yellow horse, uneasily. Muldoon kept behind him so that he could not run away.

"I know it. There must be some pore delooded fool in this State hez a right to the loose end o' your hitchin'-strap. I'm blame sorry fer him, but he shall hev his rights when we're through with you," said Rod.

"If it's all the same, gentlemen, I'd ruther change pasture. Guess I'll do it now."

"Can't always have your 'druthers. Guess you won't," said Rod,

"But look a-here. All of you ain't so blame unfriendly to a stranger. S'pose we count noses."

"What in Vermont fer?" said Rod, putting up his eyebrows. The idea of settling a question by counting noses is the very last thing that ever enters the head of a well-broken horse.

"To see how many's on my side. Here's Miss Tuck, anyway an' Colonel Tweezy yonder's neutral; an' Judge Marcus, an' I guess the Reverend [the yellow horse meant the Deacon] might see that I had my rights. He's the likeliest-lookin' trotter I've ever set eyes on. Pshaw, boys! You ain't goin' to pound *me*, be you? Why, we've gone round in pasture, all colts together, this month o' Sundays, hain't we, as friendly as could be. There ain't a horse alive – I don't care

45

who he is – has a higher opinion o' you, Mr. Rod, than I have. Let's do it fair an' true an' above the exe. Let's count noses same's they do in Kansas." Here he dropped his voice a little and turned to Marcus: "Say, Judge, there's some green food I know, back o' the brook, no one hain't touched yet. After this little *fracas* is fixed up, you an' me'll make up a party an 'tend to it."

Marcus did not answer for a long time, then he said: "There's a pup up to the haouse 'bout eight weeks old. He'll yap till he gits a lickin', an' when he sees it comin' he lies on his back an' yowls. But he don't go through no cir*kit*uous nose-counting first. I've seen a noo light sence Rod spoke. You'll better stand up to what's served. I'm goin' to philosophise all over your carcass."

"*I*'m goin' to do yer up in brown paper," said Muldoon. "I can fit you on apologies."

"Hold on. Ef we all biffed you now, these same men you've been so dead anxious to kill 'ud call us off. Guess we'll wait till they go back to the haouse, an' you'll have time to think cool an' quiet," said Rod.

"Have you no respec' whatever fer the dignity o' our common horsehood?" the yellow horse squealed.

"Nary respec" onless the horse kin do something. America's paved with the kind er horse you are – jist plain yaller-dog horse – waitin' ter be whipped inter shape. We call 'em yearlings an' colts when they're young. When they're aged we pound 'em – in this pastur'. Horse, sonny, is what you start from. We know all about horse here, an' he ain't any high-toned, pure-souled child o' nature. Horse, plain horse, same ez you, is chock-full o' tricks, an' meannesses, an' cussednesses, an' shirkin's, an' monkey-shines, which he's took over from his sire an' his dam, an' thickened up with his own special fancy in the way o' goin' crooked. Thet's *horse*, an' thet's about his dignity an' the size of his soul 'fore he's been broke an' raw-hided a piece. Now we ain't goin' to give ornery unswitched *horse*, that hain't done nawthin' wuth a quart of oats sence he wuz foaled, pet names that would be good enough fer Nancy Hanks, or Alix, or Directum, who *hev*. Don't you try to back off acrost them rocks. Wait where

46

you are! Ef I let my Hambeltonian temper git the better o' me I'd frazzle you out finer than rye-straw inside o' three minutes, you woman-scarin', kid-killin', dash-breakin', un-broke, unshod, ungaited, pastur'-hoggin', saw-backed, shark-mouthed, hair-trunk-thrown-in-in-trade son of a bronco an' a sewin'-machine!"

"I think we'd better get home," I said to my companion when Rod had finished; and we climbed into the coupé, Tedda whinnying, as we bumped over the ledges: "Well, I'm dreffle sorry I can't stay fer the sociable; but I hope an' trust my friends 'll take a ticket fer me."

"But your natchul!" said Muldoon, cheerfully, and the horses scattered before us, trotting into the ravine.

*   *   *

Next morning we sent back to the livery-stable what was left of the yellow horse. It seemed tired, but anxious to go.

4

THE MALTESE CAT

There is little to say about this story which has not already been said before many times over, save to repeat the verdict of Lord Birkenhead when he called it, "The finest description of a game in the English language."

It owes its origin, as already mentioned, to *A Walking Delegate*. That story woke in Kipling a remembrance of his own early efforts at polo when he first came to India and of his grey pony "Dolly Bobs" whom he used as his model and inspiration for the Cat. There is, incidentally, a drawing by his father, Lockwood Kipling, of one of his early efforts on the polo ground in India.

Strangely Kipling appears never to have written about polo in any of his poems, not even in his *Verses On Games* published about the same time as the Cat, although fox-hunting, as we shall see, and racing, as we have seen, did occupy him both in prose and verse.

Although it has to do with fox-hunting it seems appropriate to show his appreciation of the understanding between horse and man requisite for the utmost accomplishment of both, which also shines through *The Maltese Cat*, to include here the opening verse of his poem *Together*:

When horse and rider can trust each other everywhere, it takes a fence and more than a fence to pound that happy pair;

For the one will do what the other demands, although he is beaten and blown,

And when it is done, they can live through a run that neither could face alone.

THE MALTESE CAT

They had good reason to be proud, and better reason to be afraid, all twelve of them; for though they had fought their way, game by game, up the teams entered for the polo tournament, they were meeting the Archangels that afternoon in the final match; and the Archangels men were playing with half-a-dozen ponies apiece. As the game was divided into six quarters of eight minutes each, that meant a fresh pony after every halt. The Skidars' team, even supposing there were no accidents, could only supply one pony for every other change; and two to one is heavy odds. Again, as Shiraz, the grey Syrian, pointed out, they were meeting the pink and pick of the polo-ponies of Upper India; ponies that had cost from a thousand rupees each, while they themselves were a cheap lot gathered, often from country carts, by their masters who belonged to a poor but honest native infantry regiment.

"Money means pace and weight," said Shiraz, rubbing his black silk nose dolefully along his neat-fitting boot, "and by the maxims of the game as I know it –"

"Ah, but we aren't playing the maxims," said the Maltese Cat. "We're playing the game, and we've the great advantage of knowing the game. Just think a stride, Shiraz. We've pulled up from bottom to second place in two weeks against all those fellows on the ground here; and that's because we play with our heads as well as with our feet."

"It makes me feel undersized and unhappy all the same," said Kittiwynk, a mouse-coloured mare with a red browband and the cleanest pair of legs that ever an aged pony owned. "They've twice our size, these others."

Kittiwynk looked at the gathering and sighed. The hard, dusty Umballa polo-ground was lined with thousands of soldiers, black and white, not counting hundreds and hundreds of carriages, and drags, and dog-carts, and ladies with brilliant-coloured parasols, and officers in uniform and out of it, and crowds of natives behind them; and orderlies on camels who had halted to watch the game, instead of carrying letters up and down the station, and native horse-dealers running about on thin-eared Biluchi mares, looking for a chance to sell a few first-class polo ponies. Then there were the ponies of thirty teams that had entered for the Upper India Free For All Cup – nearly every pony of worth and dignity from Mhow to Peshawar, from Allahabad to Multan; prize ponies, Arabs, Syrian, Barb, country bred, Deccanee, Waziri, and Kabul ponies of every colour and shape and temper that you could imagine. Some of them were in mat-roofed stables close to the polo-ground, but most were under saddle while their masters, who had been defeated in the earlier games, trotted in and out and told each other exactly how the game should be played.

It was a glorious sight, and the come-and-go of the little quick hoofs, and the incessant salutations of ponies that had met before on other polo-grounds or racecourses, were enough to drive a four-footed thing wild.

But the Skidars' team were careful not to know their neighbours, though half the ponies on the ground were anxious to scrape acquaintance with the little fellows that had come from the North and, so far, had swept the board.

"Let's see," said a soft, golden-coloured Arab, who had been playing very badly the day before, to the Maltese Cat, "didn't we meet in Abdul Rahman's stable in Bombay four seasons ago? I won the Paikpattan Cup next season, you may remember."

"Not me," said the Maltese Cat politely. "I was at Malta then, pulling a vegetable cart. I don't race. I play the game."

"O-oh!" said the Arab, cocking his tail and swaggering off.

"Keep yourselves to yourselves," said the Maltese Cat to his companions. "We don't want to rub noses with all those goose-rumped half-breeds of Upper India. When we've won this cup they'll give their shoes to know us."

"*We* shan't win the cup," said Shiraz. "How do you feel?"

"Stale as last night's feed when a musk-rat has run over it," said Polaris, a rather heavy-shouldered grey, and the rest of the team agreed with him.

"The sooner you forget that the better," said the Maltese Cat cheerfully. "They've finished tiffin in the big tent. We shall be wanted now. If your saddles are not comfy, kick. If your bits aren't easy, rear, and let the *saises* know whether your boots are tight."

Each pony had his *sais*, his groom, who lived and ate and slept with the pony, and had betted a great deal more than he could afford on the result of the game. There was no chance of anything going wrong, and, to make sure, each *sais* was shampooing the legs of his pony to the last minute. Behind the *saises* sat as many of the Skidars' regiment as had leave to attend the match – about half the native officers, and a hundred or two dark, black-bearded men with the regimental pipers nervously fingering the big be-ribboned bagpipes. The Skidars were what they call a Pioneer regiment; and the bag-pipes made the national music of half the men. The native officers held bundles of polo-sticks, long cane-handled mallets, and as the grand-stand filled after lunch they arranged themselves by ones and twos at different points round the ground, so that if a stick were broken the player would not have far to ride for a new one. An impatient British cavalry band struck up "If you want to know the time, ask a p'leece-man!" and the two umpires in light dust-coats danced out on two little excited ponies. The four players of the Archangels' team followed, and the sight of their beautiful mounts made Shiraz groan again.

"Wait till we know," said the Maltese Cat. "Two of 'em are playing in blinkers, and that means they can't see to get out of the way of their own side, or they *may* shy at the umpires' ponies. They've *all* got white web reins that are sure to stretch or slip!"

"And," said Kittiwynk, dancing to take the stiffness out of her, "they carry their whips in their hands instead of on their wrists. Hah!"

"True enough. No man can manage his stick and his reins and his whip that way," said the Maltese Cat. "I've fallen over every square yard of the Malta ground, and *I* ought to know." He quivered his little flea-bitten withers just to show how satisfied he felt; but his heart was not so light. Ever since he had drifted into India on a troopship, taken, with an old rifle, as part payment for a racing debt, the Maltese Cat had played and preached polo to the Skidars' team on the Skidars' stony polo-ground. Now a polo-pony is like a poet. If he is born with a love for the game he can be made. The Maltese Cat knew that bamboos grew solely in order that polo-balls might be turned from their roots, that grain was given to ponies to keep them in hard condition, and that ponies were shod to prevent them slipping on a turn. But, besides all these things, he knew every trick and device of the finest game of the world, and for two seasons he had been teaching the others all he knew or guessed.

"Remember," he said for the hundredth time as the riders came up, "we *must* play together, and you *must* play with your heads. Whatever happens, follow the ball. Who goes out first?"

Kittiwynk, Shiraz, Polaris, and a short high little bay fellow with tremendous hocks and no withers worth speaking of (he was called Corks) were being girthed up, and the soldiers in the background stared with all their eyes.

"I want you men to keep quiet," said Lutyens, the captain of the team, "and especially *not* to blow your pipes."

"Not if we win, Captain Sahib?" asked a piper.

"If we win, you can do what you please," said Lutyens, with a smile, as he slipped the loop of his stick over his wrist, and wheeled to canter to his place. The Archangels' ponies were a little bit above themselves on account of the many-coloured crowd so close to the ground. Their riders were excellent players, but they were a team of crack players instead of a crack team; and that made all the difference in the world. They honestly meant to play together, but it is very hard for four men, each the best of the team he is picked from, to remember that in polo no brilliancy of hitting or riding makes up for playing alone. Their captain shouted his orders to them by name, and it is a curious thing that if you call his name aloud in public after an Englishman you make him hot and fretty. Lutyens said nothing to his men because it had all been said before. He pulled up Shiraz, for he was playing "back," to guard the goal. Powell on Polaris was half-back, and Macnamara and Hughes on Corks and Kittiwynk were forwards. The tough bamboo-root ball was put into the middle of the ground one hundred and fifty yards from the ends, and Hughes crossed sticks, heads-up, with the captain of the Archangels, who saw fit to play forward, and that is a place from which you cannot easily control the team. The little click as the cane-shafts met were heard all over the ground, and then Hughes made some sort of quick wrist-stroke that just dribbled the ball a few yards. Kittiwynk knew that stroke of old, and followed as a cat follows a mouse. While the captain of the Archangels was wrenching his pony round Hughes struck with all his strength, and next instant Kittiwynk was away, Corks following close behind her, their little feet pattering like rain-drops on glass.

"Pull out to the left," said Kittiwynk between her teeth, "it's coming our way, Corks!"

The back and half-back of the Archangels were tearing down on her just as she was within reach of the ball. Hughes leaned forward with a loose rein, and cut it away to the left almost under Kittiwynk's feet, and it hopped and skipped off to Corks, who saw that, if he were not quick, it would run beyond the boundaries. That long bouncing drive gave the Archangels time to wheel and send three men across the ground to head off Corks. Kittiwynk stayed where she was, for she knew the game. Corks was on the ball half a fraction of a second before the others came up, and Macnamara, with a back-handed stroke, sent it back across the ground to Hughes, who saw the way clear to the Archangels' goal, and smacked the ball in before any one quite knew what had happened.

"That's luck," said Corks, as they changed ends. "A goal in three minutes for three hits and no riding to speak of."

"Don't know," said Polaris. "We've made 'em angry too soon. Shouldn't wonder if they try to rush us off our feet next time."

"Keep the ball hanging then," said Shiraz. "That wears out every pony that isn't used to it."

Next time there was no easy galloping across the ground. All the Archangels closed up as one man, but there they stayed, for Corks, Kittiwynk, and Polaris were somewhere

53

on the top of the ball, marking time among the rattling sticks, while Shiraz circled about outside, waiting for a chance.

"*We* can do this all day," said Polaris, ramming his quarters into the side of another pony. "Where do you think you're shoving to?"

"I'll – I'll be driven in an *ekka* if I know," was the gasping reply, "and I'd give a week's feed to get my blinkers off. I can't see anything."

"The dust is rather bad. Whew! That was one for my off hock. Where's the ball, Corks?"

"Under my tail. At least a man's looking for it there. This is beautiful. They can't use their sticks, and it's driving 'em wild. Give old blinkers a push and he'll go over!"

"Here, don't touch me! I can't see. I'll – I'll back out, I think," said the pony in blinkers, who knew that if you can't see all round your head you cannot prop yourself against a shock.

Corks was watching the ball where it lay in the dust close to his near fore with Macnamara's shortened stick tap-tapping it from time to time. Kittiwynk was edging her way out of the scrimmage, whisking her stump of a tail with nervous excitement.

"Ho! They've got it," she snorted. "Let me out!" and she galloped like a rifle-bullet just behind a tall lanky pony of the Archangels, whose rider was swinging up his stick for a stroke.

"Not to-day, thank you," said Hughes, as the blow slid off his raised stick, and Kittiwynk laid her shoulder to the tall pony's quarters, and shoved him aside just as Lutyens on Shiraz sent the ball where it had come from, and the tall pony went skating and slipping away to the left. Kittiwynk, seeing that Polaris had joined Corks in the chase for the ball up the ground, dropped into Polaris's place, and then time was called.

The Skidars' ponies wasted no time in kicking or fuming. They knew each minute's rest meant so much gain, and trotted off to the rails and their *saises*, who began to scrape and blanket and rub them at once.

"Whew!" said Corks, stiffening up to get all the tickle out of the big vulcanite scraper. "If we were playing pony for pony we'd bend those Archangels double in half an hour. But they'll bring out fresh ones and fresh ones, and fresh ones after that – you see."

"Who cares?" said Polaris. "We've drawn first blood. Is my hock swelling?"

"Looks puffy," said Corks. "You must have had rather a wipe. Don't let it stiffen. You'll be wanted again in half an hour."

"What's the game like?" said the Maltese Cat.

"Ground's like your shoe, except where they've put too much water on it," said Kittiwynk. 'Then it's slippery. Don't play in the centre. There's a bog there. I don't know how their next four are going to behave, but we kept the ball hanging and made 'em lather for nothing. Who goes out? Two Arabs and a couple of countrybreds! That's bad. What a comfort it is to wash your mouth out!"

Kitty was talking with the neck of a leather-covered soda-water bottle between her teeth and trying to look over her withers at the same time. This gave her a very coquettish air.

"What's bad?" said Gray Dawn, giving to the girth and admiring his well-set shoulders.

"You Arabs can't gallop fast enough to keep yourselves warm – that's what Kitty means," said Polaris, limping to show that his hock needed attention. "Are you playing 'back,' Gray Dawn?"

"Looks like it," said Gray Dawn, as Lutyens swung himself up. Powell mounted the Rabbit, a plain bay countrybred much like Corks, but with mulish ears. Macnamara took Faiz Ullah, a handy short-backed little red Arab with a long tail, and Hughes mounted Benami, an old and sullen brown beast, who stood over in front more than a polo-pony should.

"Benami looks like business," said Shiraz. "How's your temper, Ben?" The old campaigner hobbled off without answering, and the Maltese Cat looked at the new Archangel ponies prancing about on the ground. They were four beautiful blacks, and they saddled big enough and strong enough to eat the Skidars' team and gallop away with the meal inside them.

"Blinkers again," said the Maltese Cat. "Good enough!"

"They're chargers – cavalry chargers!" said Kittiwynk indignantly. *"They'll* never see thirteen-three again."

"They've all been fairly measured and they've all got their certificates," said the Maltese Cat, "or they wouldn't be here. We must take things as they come along, and keep our eyes on the ball."

The game began, but this time the Skidars were penned to their own end of the ground, and the watching ponies did not approve of that.

"Faiz Ullah is shirking, as usual," said Polaris, with a scornful grunt.

"Faiz Ullah is eating whip," said Corks. They could hear the leather-thonged polo-quirt lacing the little fellow's well-rounded barrel. Then the Rabbit's shrill neigh came across the ground. "I can't do all the work," he cried.

"Play the game, don't talk," the Maltese Cat whickered; and all the ponies wriggled with excitement, and the soldiers and the grooms gripped the railings and shouted. A black pony with blinkers had singled out old Benami, and was interfering with him in every possible way. They could see Benami shaking his head up and down and flapping his underlip.

"There'll be a fall in a minute," said Polaris. "Benami is getting stuffy."

The game flickered up and down between goal-post and goal-post, and the black ponies were getting more confident as they felt they had the legs of the others. The ball was hit out of a little scrimmage, and Benami and the Rabbit followed it; Faiz Ullah only too glad to be quiet for an instant.

The blinkered black pony came up like a hawk, with two of his own side behind him, and Benami's eye glittered as he raced. The question was which pony should make way for the other; each rider was perfectly willing to risk a fall in a good cause. The black who had been driven nearly crazy by his blinkers trusted to his weight and his temper; But Benami knew how to apply his weight and how to keep his temper. They met, and there was a cloud of dust. The black was lying on his side with all the breath knocked out of his body. The Rabbit was a hundred yards up the ground with the ball, and

Benami was sitting down. He had slid nearly ten yards, but he had had his revenge, and sat cracking his nostrils till the black pony rose.

"That's what you get for interfering. Do you want any more?" said Benami, and he plunged into the game. Nothing was done because Faiz Ullah would not gallop, though Macnamara beat him whenever he could spare a second. The fall of the black pony had impressed his companions tremendously, and so the Archangels could not profit by Faiz Ullah's bad behaviour.

But as the Maltese Cat said, when time was called and the four came back blowing and dripping, Faiz Ullah ought to have been kicked all round Umballa. If he did not behave better next time, the Maltese Cat promised to pull out his Arab tail by the root and eat it.

There was no time to talk, for the third four were ordered out.

The third quarter of a game is generally the hottest, for each side thinks that the others must be pumped; and most of the winning play in a game is made about that time.

Lutyens took over the Maltese Cat with a pat and a hug, for Lutyens valued him more than anything else in the world. Powell had Shikast, a little grey rat with no pedigree and no manners outside polo; Macnamara mounted Bamboo, the largest of the team, and Hughes took Who's Who, *alias* The Animal. He was supposed to have Australian blood in his veins, but he looked like a clothes-horse, and you could whack him on the legs with an iron crow-bar without hurting him.

They went out to meet the very flower of the Archangels' team, and when Who's Who saw their elegantly booted legs and their beautiful satiny skins he grinned a grin through his light, well-worn bridle.

"My word!" said Who's Who. "We must give 'em a little football. Those gentlemen need a rubbing down."

"No biting," said the Maltese Cat warningly, for once or twice in his career Who's Who had been known to forget himself in that way.

"Who said anything about biting? I'm not playing tiddly-winks. I'm playing the game."

The Archangels came down like a wolf on the fold, for they were tired of football and they wanted polo. They got it more and more. Just after the game began, Lutyens hit a ball that was coming towards him rapidly, and it rose in the air, as a ball sometimes will, with the whirr of a frightened partridge. Shikast heard, but could not see it for the minute, though he looked everywhere and up into the air as the Maltese Cat had taught him. When he saw it ahead and overhead, he went forward with Powell as fast as he could put foot to ground. It was then that Powell, a quiet and level-headed man as a rule, became inspired and played a stroke that sometimes comes off successfully on a quiet afternoon of long practice. He took his stick in both hands, and standing up in his stirrups, swiped at the ball in the air, Munipore fashion. There was one second of paralysed astonishment, and then all four sides of the ground went up in a yell of applause and delight as the ball flew true (you could see the amazed Archangels ducking in their saddles to get out of the line of flight, and looking at it with open mouths), and the regimental pipes of the Skidars squealed from the railings as long as the pipers had breath.

Shikast heard the stroke; but he heard the head of the stick fly off at the same time. Nine hundred and ninety-nine ponies out of a thousand would have gone tearing on after the ball with a useless player pulling at their heads, but Powell knew him, and he knew Powell; and the instant he felt Powell's right leg shift a trifle on the saddle-flap he headed to the boundary, where a native officer was frantically waving a new stick. Before the shouts had ended Powell was armed again.

Once before in his life the Maltese Cat had heard that very same stroke played off his own back, and had profited by the confusion it made. This time he acted on experience, and leaving Bamboo to guard the goal in case of accidents, came through the others like a flash, head and tail low, Lutyens standing up to ease him – swept on and on before the other side knew what was the matter, and nearly pitched on his head between the Archangels' goal-posts as Lutyens tipped the ball in after a straight scurry of a hundred and fifty yards. If there was one thing more than another upon which the

Maltese Cat prided himself it was on this quick, streaking kind of run half across the ground. He did not believe in taking balls round the field unless you were clearly over-matched. After this they gave the Archangels five minutes' football, and an expensive fast pony hates football because it rumples his temper.

Who's Who showed himself even better than Polaris in this game. He did not permit any wriggling away, but bored joyfully into the scrimmage as if he had his nose in a feed-box, and were looking for something nice. Little Shikast jumped on the ball the minute it got clear, and every time an Archangel pony followed it he found Shikast standing over it asking what was the matter.

"If we can live through this quarter," said the Maltese Cat, "I shan't care. Don't take it out of yourselves. Let them do the lathering."

So the ponies, as their riders explained afterwards, "shut up." The Archangels kept them tied fast in front of their goal, but it cost the Archangels' ponies all that was left of their tempers; and ponies began to kick, and men began to repeat compliments, and they chopped at the legs of Who's Who, and he set his teeth and stayed where he was, and the dust stood up like a tree over the scrimmage till that hot quarter ended.

They found the ponies very excited and confident when they went to their *saises*; and the Maltese Cat had to warn them that the worst of the game was coming.

"Now *we* are all going in for the second time," said he, "and *they* are trotting out fresh ponies. You'll think you can gallop, but you'll find you can't; and then you'll be sorry.'

"But two goals to nothing is a halter-long lead," said Kitti-wynk prancing.

"How long does it take to get a goal?" the Maltese Cat answered. "For pity sake, don't run away with the notion that the game is half-won just because we happen to be in luck now. They'll ride you into the grand-stand if they can; you must *not* give 'em a chance. Follow the ball."

"Football, as usual?" said Polaris. "My hock's half as big as a nose-bag."

"Don't let them have a look at the ball if you can help it.

59

Now leave me alone. I must get all the rest I can before the last quarter."

He hung down his head and let all his muscles go slack; Shikast, Bamboo, and Who's Who copying his example.

"Better not watch the game," he said. "We aren't playing, and we shall only take it out of ourselves if we grow anxious. Look at the ground and pretend it's fly-time."

They did their best, but it was hard advice to follow. The hoofs were drumming and the sticks were rattling all up and down the ground, and yells of applause from the English troops told that the Archangels were pressing the Skidars hard. The native soldiers behind the ponies groaned and grunted, and said things in undertones, and presently they heard a long-drawn shout and a clatter of hurrahs!

"One to the Archangels," said Shikast, without raising his head. "Time's nearly up. Oh, my sire and dam!"

"Faiz Ullah," said the Maltese Cat, "if you don't play to the last nail in your shoes this time, I'll kick you on the ground before all the other ponies."

"I'll do my best when my time comes," said the little Arab sturdily.

The *saises* looked at each other gravely as they rubbed their ponies' legs. This was the first time when long purses began to tell, and everybody knew it. Kittiwynk and the others came back with the sweat dripping over their hoofs and their tails telling sad stories.

"They're better than we are," said Shiraz. "I knew how it would be."

"Shut your big head," said the Maltese Cat; "we've one goal to the good yet."

"Yes, but it's two Arabs and two countrybreds to play now," said Corks. "Faiz Ullah, remember!" He spoke in a biting voice.

As Lutyens mounted Gray Dawn he looked at his men, and they did not look pretty. They were covered with dust and sweat in streaks. Their yellow boots were almost black, their wrists were red and lumpy, and their eyes seemed two inches deep in their heads, but the expression in the eyes was satisfactory.

60

"Did you take anything at tiffin?" said Lutyens, and the team shook their heads. They were too dry to talk.

"All right. The Archangels did. They are worse pumped than we are."

"They've got the better ponies," said Powell. "I shan't be sorry when this business is over."

That fifth quarter was a sad one in every way. Faiz Ullah played like a little red demon; and the Rabbit seemed to be everywhere at once, and Benami rode straight at anything and everything that came in his way, while the umpires on their ponies wheeled like gulls outside the shifting game. But the Archangels had the better mounts – they had kept their racers till late in the game – and never allowed the Skidars to play football. They hit the ball up and down the width of the ground till Benami and the rest were outpaced. Then they went forward, and time and again Lutyens and Gray Dawn were just, and only just, able to send the ball away with a long splitting back-hander. Gray Dawn forgot that he was an Arab; and turned from gray to blue as he galloped. Indeed, he forgot too well, for he did not keep his eyes on the ground as an Arab should, but stuck out his nose and scuttled for the dear honour of the game. They had watered the ground once or twice between the quarters, and a careless waterman had emptied the last of his skinful all in one place near the Skidars' goal. It was close to the end of play, and for the tenth time Gray Dawn was bolting after a ball when his near hind foot slipped on the greasy mud and he rolled over and over, pitching Lutyens just clear of the goal-post; and the triumphant Archangels made their goal. Then time was called – two goals all; but Lutyens had to be helped up, and Gray Dawn rose with his near hind leg strained somewhere.

"What's the damage?" said Powell, his arm round Lutyens.

"Collar-bone, of course," said Lutyens between his teeth. It was the third time he had broken it in two years, and it hurt him.

Powell and the others whistled. "Game's up," said Hughes.

"Hold on. We've five good minutes yet, and it isn't my right hand," said Lutyens. "We'll stick it out."

61

"I say," said the captain of the Archangels, trotting up. "Are you hurt, Lutyens? We'll wait if you care to put in a substitute. I wish – I mean – the fact is, you fellows deserve this game if any team does. Wish we could give you a man or some of our ponies – or something."

"You're awfully good, but we'll play it to a finish, I think."

The captain of the Archangels stared for a little, "That's not half bad," he said, and went back to his own side, while Lutyens borrowed a scarf from one of his native officers and made a sling of it. Then an Archangel galloped up with a big bath sponge and advised Lutyens to put it under his arm-pit to ease his shoulder, and between them they tied up his left arm scientifically, and one of the native officers leaped forward with four long glasses that fizzed and bubbled.

The team looked at Lutyens piteously, and he nodded. It was the last quarter, and nothing would matter after that. They drank out the dark golden drink, and wiped their moustaches, and things looked more hopeful.

The Maltese Cat had put his nose into the front of Lutyens' shirt, and was trying to say how sorry he was.

"He knows," said Lutyens, proudly. "The beggar knows. I've played him without a bridle before now – for fun."

"It's no fun now," said Powell. "But we haven't a decent substitute."

"No," said Lutyens. "It's the last quarter, and we've got to make our goal and win. I'll trust the Cat."

"If you fall this time you'll suffer a little," said Macnamara.

"I'll trust the Cat," said Lutyens.

"You hear that?" said the Maltese Cat proudly to the others. "It's worth while playing polo for ten years to have that said of you. Now then, my sons, come along. We'll kick up a little bit, just to show the Archangels *this* team haven't suffered."

And, sure enough, as they went on to the ground the Maltese Cat, after satisfying himself that Lutyens was home in the saddle, kicked out three or four times, and Lutyens laughed. The reins were caught up anyhow in the tips of his strapped hand, and he never pretended to rely on them. He knew the Cat would answer to the least pressure of the leg, and by way of showing off – for his shoulder hurt him very much – he bent the little fellow in a close figure-of-eight in and out between the goal-posts. There was a roar from the native officers and men, who dearly loved a piece of *duga-bashi* (horse-trick work), as they called it, and the pipes very quietly and scornfully droned out the first bars of a common bazaar-tune called "Freshly Fresh and Newly New," just as a warning to the other regiments that the Skidars were fit. All the natives laughed.

"And now," said the Cat, as they took their place, "remember that this is the last quarter, and follow the ball!"

"Don't need to be told," said Who's Who.'

"Let me go on. All those people on all four sides will begin to crowd in – just as they did at Malta. You'll hear people calling out, and moving forward and being pushed back, and that is going to make the Archangel ponies very unhappy. But if a ball is struck to the boundary, you go after it, and let the people get out of your way. I went over the pole of a four-in-hand once, and picked a game out of the dust by it. Back me up when I run, and follow the ball."

There was a sort of an all-round sound of sympathy and wonder as the last quarter opened, and then there began exactly what the Maltese Cat had foreseen. People crowded in close to the boundaries, and the Archangels' ponies kept looking sideways at the narrowing space. If you know how a man feels to be cramped at tennis – not because he wants to run out of the court, but because he likes to know that he can at a pinch – you will guess how ponies must feel when they are playing in a box of human beings.

"I'll bend some of those men if I can get away," said Who's Who, as he rocketed behind the ball; and Bamboo nodded without speaking. They were playing the last ounce in them, and the Maltese Cat had left the goal undefended to join them. Lutyens gave him every order that he could to bring him back, but this was the first time in his career that the little wise gray had ever played polo on his own responsibility, and he was going to make the most of it.

"What are you doing here?" said Hughes, as the Cat crossed in front of him and rode off an Archangel.

"The Cat's in charge – mind the goal!" shouted Lutyens, and bowing forward hit the ball full, and followed on, forcing the Archangels towards their own goal.

"No football," said the Cat. "Keep the ball by the boundaries and cramp 'em. Play open order and drive 'em to the boundaries."

Across and across the ground in big diagonals flew the ball, and whenever it came to a flying rush and a stroke close to the boundaries the Archangel ponies moved stiffly. They did not care to go headlong at a wall of men and carriages, though if the ground had been open they could have turned on a sixpence.

"Wriggle her up the sides," said the Cat. "Keep her close to the crowd. They hate the carriages. Shikast, keep her up this side."

Shikast with Powell lay left and right behind the uneasy scuffle of an open scrimmage, and every time the ball was hit away Shikast galloped on it at such an angle that Powell was forced to hit it towards the boundary; and when the crowd had been driven away from that side, Lutyens would send the ball over to the other, and Shikast would slide desperately after it till his friends came down to help. It was billiards, and no football, this time – billiards in a corner pocket; and the cues were not well chalked.

"If they get us out in the middle of the ground they'll walk away from us. Dribble her along the sides," cried the Cat.

So they dribbled all along the boundary, where a pony could not come on their right-hand side; and the Archangels were furious, and the umpires had to neglect the game to shout at the people to get back, and several blundering mounted policemen tried to restore order, all close to the scrimmage, and the nerves of the Archangels' ponies stretched and broke like cobwebs.

Five or six times an Archangel hit the ball up into the middle of the ground, and each time the watchful Shikast gave Powell his chance to send it back, and after each return, when the dust had settled, men could see that the Skidars had gained a few yards.

Every now and again there were shouts of " 'Side! Off

side!" from the spectators; but the teams were too busy to care, and the umpires had all they could do to keep their maddened ponies clear of the scuffle.

At last Lutyens missed a short easy stroke, and the Skidars had to fly back helter-skelter to protect their own goal, Shikast leading. Powell stopped the ball with a backhander when it was not fifty yards from the goal-post, and Shikast spun round with a wrench that nearly hoisted Powell out of his saddle.

"Now's our last chance," said the Cat, wheeling like a cockchafer on a pin. "We've got to ride it out. Come along."

Lutyens felt the little chap take a deep breath, and, as it were, crouch under his rider. The ball was hopping towards the right-hand boundary, an Archangel riding for it with both spurs and a whip; but neither spur nor whip would make this pony stretch himself as he neared the crowd. The Maltese Cat glided under his very nose, picking up his hind legs sharp, for there was not a foot to spare between his quarters and the other pony's bit. It was as neat an exhibition as fancy figure-skating. Lutyens hit with all the strength he had left, but the stick slipped a little in his hand, and the ball flew off to the left instead of keeping close to the boundary. Who's Who was far across the ground, thinking hard as he galloped. He repeated, stride for stride, the Cat's manœuvres, with another Archangel pony, nipping the ball away from under his bridle, and clearing his opponent by half a fraction of an inch, for Who's Who was clumsy behind. Then he drove away towards the right as the Maltese Cat came up from the left; and Bamboo held a middle course exactly between them. The three were making a sort of Government-broad-arrow-shaped attack; and there was only the Arch-angels' back to guard the goal; but immediately behind them were three Archangels racing all they knew, and mixed up with them was Powell, sending Shikast along on what he felt was their last hope. It takes a very good man to stand up to the rush of seven crazy ponies in the last quarter of a cup game, when men are riding with their necks for sale, and the ponies are delirious. The Archangels' back missed his stroke, and pulled aside just in time to let the rush go by. Bamboo and Who's Who shortened stride to give the Maltese Cat room, and Lutyens got the goal with a clean, smooth, smacking stroke that was heard all over the field. But there was no stopping the ponies. They poured through the goal-posts in one mixed mob, winners and losers together, for the pace had been terrific. The Maltese Cat knew by experience what would happen, and, to save Lutyens, turned to the right with one last effort that strained a back-sinew beyond hope of repair. As he did so he heard the right-hand goal-post crack as a pony cannoned into it – crack, splinter, and fall like a mast. It had been sawed three parts through in case of accidents, but it upset the pony nevertheless, and he blundered into another, who blundered into the left-hand post, and then there was confusion and dust and wood. Bamboo was lying on the ground, seeing stars; an Archangel pony rolled beside him, breathless and angry; Shikast had sat down dog-fashion to avoid falling over the others, and was sliding along on his little bobtail in a cloud of dust; and Powell was sitting on the ground, hammering with his stick and trying to cheer. All the others were shouting at the top of what was left of their voices, and the men who had been spilt were shouting too. As soon as the people saw no one was hurt, ten thousand native and English shouted, and clapped and yelled, and before any one could stop them the pipers of the Skidars broke on to the ground, with all the native officers and men behind them, and marched up and down, playing a wild northern tune called "Zakhme Bagãn," and through the insolent blaring of the pipes and the high-pitched native yells you could hear the Archangels' band hammering, "For they are all jolly good fellows," and then reproachfully to the losing team, "Ooh, Kafoozalum! Kafoozalum! Kafoozalum!"

Besides all these things and many more, there was a Commander-in-Chief, and an Inspector-General of Cavalry, and the principal veterinary officer in all India, standing on the top of a regimental coach, yelling like school-boys; and brigadiers and colonels and commissioners, and hundreds of pretty ladies joined the chorus. But the Maltese Cat stood with his head down, wondering how many legs were left to

him; and Lutyens watched the men and ponies pick themselves out of the wreck of the two goal-posts, and he patted
the Cat very tenderly.

"I say," said the captain of the Archangels, spitting a
pebble out of his mouth, "will you take three thousand for
that pony – as he stands?"

"No, thank you. I've an idea he's saved my life," said
Lutyens, getting off and lying down at full length. Both
teams were on the ground too, waving their boots in the air,
and coughing and drawing deep breaths, as the *saises* ran up
to take away the ponies, and an officious water-carrier
sprinkled the players with dirty water till they sat up.

"My Aunt!" said Powell, rubbing his back and looking at
the stumps of the goal-posts, "that was a game!"

They played it over again, every stroke of it, that night at the
big dinner, when the Free-for-All Cup was filled and passed
down the table, and emptied and filled again, and everybody
made most eloquent speeches. About two in the morning,
when there might have been some singing, a wise little, plain
little, gray little head looked in through the open door.

"Hurrah! Bring him in," said the Archangels; and his *sais*,
who was very happy indeed, patted the Maltese Cat on the
flank, and he limped in to the blaze of light and the glittering
of uniforms, looking for Lutyens. He was used to messes, and
men's bedrooms, and places where ponies are not usually encouraged, and in his youth had jumped on and off a mess-table
for a bet. So he behaved himself very politely, and ate bread
dipped in salt, and was petted all round the table, moving
gingerly; and they drank his health, because he had done
more to win the Cup than any man or horse on the ground.

That was glory and honour enough for the rest of his days,
and the Maltese Cat did not complain much when his veterinary surgeon said that he would be no good for polo any
more. When Lutyens married, his wife did not allow him to
play, so he was forced to be an umpire; and his pony on
these occasions was a flea-bitten gray with a neat polo-tail,
lame all round, but desperately quick on his feet, and, as
everybody knew, Past Pluperfect Prestissimo Player of the
Game.

5

THE BALLAD OF EAST AND WEST

This is probably one of the best things Kipling ever wrote. Not only does it mark the transition of his light verse into true poetry and contain some of his most memorable lines, it shows, too, his love and understanding of horses in his description of the two differing animals ridden respectively by Kamal, the horse-thief, and the Colonel's son, and the way they ran in the hot pursuit. Like so many of Kipling's stories and verses it is based on a true incident which happened on the Frontier in 1848. The thief was a marauder, Dilawar Khan, and the Colonel, Lumsden of the Guides, a name known in racing circles to this day.

First published in the November issue of *Macmillan's Magazine* in 1898 under the pseudonym of "Tussuf", which did not conceal the author's identity for very long, it attracted immediate attention. George Sainsbury, the doyen of literary critics of the day, gave it a special mention and even Tennyson, the then Poet Laureate, in his declining years, told a friend that having read it he was of the opinion Kipling was the only contemporary poet who glowed "with a divine fire." Perhaps Charles Carrington in his biography summed it up best of all when he wrote: "The subject, though painted with the local colour of northern India and painted with brilliant realism, was a human drama which is likely to attract readers as long as men admire courage and love a good horse."

THE BALLAD OF EAST AND WEST

Oh, East is East, and West is West, and never the twain shall meet.
Till Earth and Sky stand presently at God's great Judgment Seat;
But there is neither East nor West, Border, nor Breed, nor Birth,
When two strong men stand face to face, though they come from the ends of the earth!

Kamal is out with twenty men to raise the Border side,
And he has lifted the Colonel's mare that is the Colonel's pride.
He has lifted her out of the stable-door between the dawn and the day,
And turned the calkins upon her feet, and ridden her far away.
Then up and spoke the Colonel's son that led a troop of the Guides:
"Is there never a man of all my men can say where Kamal hides?"
Then up and spoke Mohammed Khan, the son of the Ressaldar:
"If ye know the track of the morning-mist, ye know where his pickets are.
"At dusk he harries the Abazai – at dawn he is into Bonair,
"But he must go by Fort Bukloh to his own place to fare.
"So if ye gallop to Fort Bukloh as fast as a bird can fly,
"By the favour of God ye may cut him off ere he win to the Tongue of Jagai.
"But if he be past the Tongue of Jagai, right swiftly turn ye then,
"For the length and the breadth of that grisly plain is sown with Kamal's men.
"There is rock to the left, and rock to the right, and low lean thorn between,
"And ye may hear a breech-bolt snick where never a man is seen."

The Colonel's son has taken horse, and a raw rough dun
was he,
With the mouth of a bell and the heart of Hell and the
head of a gallows-tree.
The Colonel's son to the Fort has won, they bid him stay
to eat –
Who rides at the tail of a Border thief, he sits not long at
his meat.
He's up and away from Fort Bukloh as fast as he can fly,
Till he was aware of his father's mare in the gut of the
Tongue of Jagai,
Till he was aware of his father's mare with Kamal upon
her back,
And when he could spy the white of her eye, he made the
pistol crack.
He has fired once, he has fired twice, but the whistling ball
went wide.
"Ye shoot like a soldier," Kamal said. "Show now if ye can
ride!"
It's up and over the Tongue of Jagai, as blown dust-devils
go,
The dun he fled like a stag of ten, but the mare like a
barren doe.
The dun he leaned against the bit and slugged his head
above,
But the red mare played with the snaffle-bars, as a maiden
plays with a glove.
There was a rock to the left and rock to the right, and low
lean thorn between,
And thrice he heard a breech-bolt snick tho' never a man
was seen.
They have ridden the low moon out of the sky, their hoofs
drum up the dawn,
The dun he went like a wounded bull, but the mare like a
new-roused fawn.
The dun he fell at a water-course – in a woeful heap fell
he,
And Kamal has turned the red mare back, and pulled the
rider free

He has knocked the pistol out of his hand – small room
     was there to strive,
"'Twas only by favour of mine," quoth he, "ye rode so
     long alive:
"There was not a rock for twenty mile, there was not a
     clump of tree,
"But covered a man of my own men with his rifle cocked
     on his knee.
"If I had raised my bridle-hand, as I have held it low,
"The little jackals that flee so fast were feasting all in a row.
"If I had bowed my head on my breast, as I have held it
     high,
"The kite that whistles above us now were gorged till she
     could not fly."
Lightly answered the Colonel's son: "Do good to bird and
     beast,
"But count who come for the broken meats before thou
     makest a feast.
"If there should follow a thousand swords to carry my
     bones away,
"Belike the price of a jackal's meal were more than a thief
     could pay
"They will feed their horse on the standing crop, their men
     on the garnered grain.
"The thatch of the byres will serve their fires when all the
     cattle are slain.
"But if thou thinkest the price is fair, – thy brethren wait
     to sup,
"The hound is kin to the jackal-spawn, – howl, dog, and
     call them up!
"And if thou thinkest the price be high, in steer and gear
     and stack,
"Give me my father's mare again, and I'll fight my own
     way back!"
Kamal has gripped him by the hand and set him upon his
     feet.
"No talk shall be of dogs," said he, "when wolf and grey
     wolf meet.
"May I eat dirt if thou hast hurt of me in deed or breath;

71

"What dam of lances brought thee forth to jest at the dawn
　　with Death?"
Lightly answered the Colonel's son: "I hold by the blood
　　of my clan:
"Take up the mare for my father's gift – by God, she has
　　carried a man!"
The red mare ran to the Colonel's son, and nuzzled against
　　his breast;
"We be two strong men," said Kamal then, "but she
　　loveth the younger best.
"So she shall go with a lifter's dower, my turquoise-
　　studded rein,
"My broidered saddle and saddle-cloth, and silver stirrups
　　twain."
The Colonel's son a pistol drew, and held it muzzle-end,
"Ye have taken the one from a foe," said he. "Will ye take
　　the mate from a friend?"
"A gift for a gift," said Kamal straight; "a limb for the risk
of a limb.
"Thy father has sent his son to me, I'll send my son to
　　him!"
With that he whistled his only son, that dropped from a
　　mountain-crest –
He trod the ling like a buck in spring, and he looked like a
　　lance in rest.
"Now here is thy master," Kamal said, "who leads a troop
　　of the Guides,
"And thou must ride at his left side as shield on shoulder
　　rides.
"Till Death or I cut loose the tie, at camp and board and
　　bed,
"Thy life is his – thy fate it is to guard him with thy
　　head.
"So, thou must eat the White Queen's meat, and all her
　　foes are thine,
"And thou must harry thy father's hold for the peace of
　　the Border-line.
"And thou must make a trooper tough and hack thy way
　　to power –

"Belike they will raise thee to Ressaldar when I am hanged
    in Peshawur!"

They have looked each other between the eyes, and there
    they found no fault.
They have taken the Oath of the Brother-in-Blood on
    leavened bread and salt:
They have taken the Oath of the Brother-in-Blood on fire
    and fresh-cut sod,
On the hilt and the haft of the Khyber knife, and the
    Wondrous Names of God.
The Colonel's son he rides the mare and Kamal's boy the
    dun,
And two have come back to Fort Bukloh where they went
    forth but one.
And when they drew to the Quarter-Guard, full twenty
    swords flew clear –
There was not a man but carried his feud with the blood of
    the mountaineer.
"Ha' done! ha' done!" said the Colonel's son. "Put up the
    steel at your sides!
"Last night ye had struck at a Border thief – to-night't is a
    man of the Guides!"
*Oh, East is East, and West is West, and never the twain shall
    meet.*
Till Earth and Sky stand presently at God's great Judgment Seat;
But there is neither East nor West, Border, nor Breed, nor Birth,
*When two strong men stand face to face, though they come from
    the ends of the earth!*

6

LITTLE FOXES

This was one of Kipling's few forays into the actual hunting field albeit in a strange land, the Sudan. As with many if not most of his stories it is founded on a *conte* related over the port by a colonial administrator who had introduced fox-hunting into his district. Kipling used it to illustrate how the popularity of the hunt brought about the fall of one of the tribe he most detested, a Liberal, do-gooding M.P., a type he had already much earlier in his Indian period, savagely casti-gated in his verses, *Pagett M.P.*, who was, "a liar and a fluent liar therewith".

Although Kipling later claimed that another fox-hunting colonial civil servant told him he had got the story just right, for purists it might have been of benefit had he checked the names he gave hounds with those on hound lists. It was perhaps another of his slip-ups in his fondness for reciting technical detail which, despite all his care, keep recurring in his work. His memory, even early on, often failed him when writing in hot heat, possessed by what he referred to as his "daemon", and he did not pause to check. But, as Sir Angus Wilson remarks in a perceptive passage: "His poor memory and inaccuracy in detail were equally marked throughout his life. In his art it has led naïve Kipling admirers to heights of admiration when he gets technical details right and puzzled disappointment when he gets them wrong. None of this matters at all, of course, for like all artists he uses the real world only as bricks to build his own imaginative construc-tions." Until the end of his life Kipling sought technical mastery of all subjects, however unlikely. In his closing years although wracked with stoically borne pain and unhappiness, this became almost an obsession. Meeting King Feisal of Iraq he cross-examined him so closely about the habits and training of camels that the King was moved to remark "Does this fellow take me for a camel-driver?"

LITTLE FOXES

A Tale of the Gihon Hunt

A fox came out of his earth on the banks of the Great River Gihon, which waters Ethiopia. He saw a white man riding through the dry dhurra-stalks, and, that his destiny might be fulfilled, barked at him.

The rider drew rein among the villagers round his stirrup.

"What," he said, "is that?"

"That," said the Sheikh of the village, "is a fox, O Excellency Our Governor."

"Is it not, then, a jackal?"

"No jackal, but Abu Hussein, the Father of Cunning."

"Also," – the white man spoke half aloud, – "I am Mudir of this Province."

"It is true," they cried. "Ya, Saart el Mudir" [O Excellency Our Governor].

The Great River Gihon, well used to the moods of kings, slid between his mile-wide banks toward the sea, while the Governor praised God in a loud and searching cry never before heard by the River.

When he had lowered his right forefinger from behind his right ear, the villagers talked to him of their crops – barley, dhurra, millet, onions, and the like. The Governor stood up in his stirrups. North he looked at a strip of green cultivation a few hundred yards wide which lay like a carpet between the river and the tawny line of the desert. Sixty miles that strip stretched before him, and as many behind. At every half-mile a groaning waterwheel lifted the soft water from the river to the crops by way of a mud-built aqueduct. A foot or so wide was the water-channel; five foot or more high was the bank on which it ran, and its base was broad in proportion. Abu Hussein, misnamed the Father of Cunning, drank from the river below his earth, and his shadow was long in the low sun. He could not understand the loud cry which the Governor had cried.

The Sheikh of the village spoke of the crops from which the rulers of all lands draw revenue; but the Governor's eyes were fixed, between his horse's ears, on the nearest water-channel.

"Very like a ditch in Ireland," he murmured, and smiled, dreaming of a razor-topped bank in distant Kildare.

Encouraged by that smile, the Sheikh continued. "When crops fail it is necessary to remit taxation. Then it is a good thing, O Excellency Our Governor, that you should come and see the crops which have failed, and discover that we have not lied."

"Assuredly." The Governor shortened his reins. The horse cantered on, rose at the embankment of the water-channel, changed leg cleverly on top, and hopped down in a cloud of golden dust.

Abu Hussein from his earth watched with interest. He had never before seen such things.

"Assuredly," the Governor repeated, and came back by the way he had gone. "It is always best to see for one's self."

An ancient and still bullet-speckled stern-wheel steamer, with a barge lashed to her side, came round the river bend. She whistled to tell the Governor his dinner was ready, and the horse, seeing his fodder piled on the barge, whinnied.

"Moreover," the Sheikh added, "in the Days of the Oppression the Emirs and their creatures dispossessed many people of their lands. All up and down the River our people are waiting to return to their lawful fields."

"Judges have been appointed to settle that matter," said the Governor. "They will presently come in steamers and hear the witnesses."

"Wherefore? Did the Judges kill the Emirs? We would rather be judged by the men who executed God's judgment on the Emirs. We would rather abide by *your* decision, O Excellency Our Governor."

76

The Governor nodded. It was a year since he had seen the Emirs stretched close and still round the reddened sheepskin where lay El Mahdi, the Prophet of God. Now there remained no trace of their dominion except the old steamer, once part of a Dervish flotilla, which was his house and office. She sidled into the shore, lowered a plank, and the Governor followed his horse aboard.

Lights burned on her till late, dully reflected in the river that tugged at her mooring-ropes. The Governor read, not for the first time, the administration reports of one John Jorrocks, M.F.H.

"We shall need," he said suddenly to his Inspector, "about ten couple. I'll get 'em when I go home. You'll be Whip, Baker?"

The Inspector, who was not yet twenty-five, signified his assent in the usual manner, while Abu Hussein barked at the vast desert moon.

"Ha!" said the Governor, coming out in his pyjamas, "we'll be giving you capivi in another three months, my friend."

*   *   *

It was four, as a matter of fact, ere a steamer with a melodious bargeful of hounds anchored at that landing. The Inspector leaped down among them, and the homesick wanderers received him as a brother.

"Everybody fed 'em everything on board ship, but they're real dainty hounds at bottom," the Governor explained. "That's Royal you've got hold of – the pick of the bunch – and the bitch that's got hold of you – she's a little excited – is May Queen. Merriman, out of Cottesmore Maudlin, you know."

"I know. 'Grand old betch with the tan eye-brows,'" the Inspector cooed. "Oh, Ben! I shall take an interest in life now. Hark to 'em! Oh, hark!"

Abu Hussein, under the high bank, went about his night's work. An eddy carried his scent to the barge, and three villages heard the crash of music that followed. Even then Abu Hussein did not know better than to bark in reply.

"Well, what about my Province?" the Governor asked.

"Not so bad," the Inspector answered, with Royal's head between his knees. "Of course, all the villages want remission of taxes, but, as far as I can see, the whole country's stinkin' with foxes. Our trouble will be choppin' 'em in cover. I've got a list of the only villages entitled to any remission. What d'you call this flat-sided, blue-mottled beast with the jowl?"

"Beagle-boy. I have my doubts about him. Do you think we can get two days a week?"

"Easy; and as many byes as you please. The Sheikh of this village here tells me that his barley has failed, and he wants a fifty per cent remission."

"We'll begin with him to-morrow, and look at his crops as we go. Nothing like personal supervision," said the Governor.

They began at sunrise. The pack flew off the barge in every direction, and, after gambols, dug like terriers at Abu Hussein's many earths. Then they drank themselves pot-bellied on Gihon water while the Governor and the Inspector chastised them with whips. Scorpions were added; for May Queen nosed one, and was removed to the barge lamenting. Mystery (a puppy, alas!) met a snake, and the blue-mottled Beagle-boy (never a dainty hound) ate that which he should have passed by. Only Royal, of the Belvoir tan head and the sad, discerning eyes, made any attempt to uphold the honour of England before the watching village.

"You can't expect everything," said the Governor after breakfast.

"We got it, though – everything except foxes. Have you seen May Queen's nose?" said the Inspector.

"And Mystery's dead. We'll keep 'em coupled next time till we get well in among the crops. I say, what a babbling body-snatcher that Beagle-boy is! Ought to be drowned!"

"They bury people so dam' casual hereabouts. Give him another chance," the Inspector pleaded, not knowing that he should live to repent most bitterly.

"Talkin' of chances," said the Governor, "this Sheikh lies about his barley bein' a failure. If it's high enough to hide a

78

hound at this time of year, it's all right. And he wants a fifty per cent remission, you said?"

"You didn't go on past the melon patch where I tried to turn Wanderer. It's all burned up from there on to the desert. His own waterwheel has broken down, too," the Inspector replied.

"Very good. We'll split the difference and allow him twenty-five per cent off. Where'll we meeet to-morrow?"

"There's some trouble among the villages down the river about their land-titles. It's good goin' about there too," the Inspector said.

The next meet, then, was some twenty miles down the river, and the pack were not enlarged till they were fairly among the fields. Abu Hussein was there in force – four of him. Four delirious hunts of four minutes each – four hounds per fox – ended in four earths just above the river. All the village looked on.

"We forgot about the earths. The banks are riddled with 'em. This'll defeat us," said the Inspector.

"Wait a moment!" The Governor drew forth a sneezing hound. "I've just remembered I'm Governor of these parts."

"Then turn out a black battalion to stop for us. We'll need 'em, old man."

The Governor straightened his back. "Give ear, O people!" he cried. "I make a new Law!"

The villagers closed in. He called: –

"Henceforward I will give one dollar to the man on whose land Abu Hussein is found. And another dollar" – he held up the coin – "to the man on whose land these dogs shall kill him. But to the man on whose land Abu Hussein shall run into a hole such as in this hole, I will not give dollars, but a most immeasurable beating. It is understood?"

"Our Excellency," – a man stepped forth – "on my land Abu Hussein was found this morning. Is it not so, brothers?"

None denied. The Governor tossed him over four dollars without a word.

"On my land they all went into their holes," cried another. "Therefore I must be beaten."

"Not so. The land is mine, and mine are the beatings."

79

This second speaker thrust forward his shoulders already bared, and the villagers shouted.

"Hullo! Two men anxious to be licked? There must be some swindle about the land," said the Governor. Then in the local vernacular: "What are your rights to the beating?"

As a river-reach changes beneath a slant of the sun, that which had been a scattered mob changed to a court of most ancient justice. The hounds tore and sobbed at Abu Hussein's hearthstone, all unnoticed among the legs of the witnesses, and Gihon, also accustomed to laws, purred approval.

"You will not wait till the Judges come up the river to settle the dispute?" said the Governor at last.

"No!" shouted all the village save the man who had first asked to be beaten. "We will abide by Our Excellency's decision. Let Our Excellency turn out the creatures of the Emirs who stole our land in the Days of the Oppression."

"And thou sayest?" the Governor turned to the man who had first asked to be beaten.

"I say *I* will wait till the wise Judges come down in the steamer. Then I will bring my many witnesses," he replied.

"He is rich. He will bring many witnesses," the village Sheikh muttered.

"No need. Thine own mouth condemns thee!" the Governor cried. "No man lawfully entitled to his land would wait one hour before entering upon it. Stand aside!" The man fell back, and the village jeered him.

The second claimant stooped quickly beneath the lifted hunting-crop. The village rejoiced.

"O Such an one; Son of such an one," said the Governor, prompted by the Sheikh, "learn, from the day when I send the order, to block up all the holes where Abu Hussein may hide – on – thy land!"

The light flicks ended. The man stood up triumphant. By that accolade had the Supreme Government acknowledged his title before all men.

While the village praised the perspicacity of the Governor, a naked, pock-marked child strode forward to the earth, and stood on one leg, unconcerned as a young stork.

80

"Ha!" he said, hands behind his back. "This should be blocked up with bundles of dhurra stalks – or, better, bundles of thorns."

"Better thorns," said the Governor. "Thick ends innermost."

The child nodded gravely and squatted on the sand.

"An evil day for thee, Abu Hussein," he shrilled into the mouth of the earth. "A day of obstacles to thy flagitious returns in the morning!"

"Who is it?" the Governor asked the Sheikh. "It thinks."

"Farag the Fatherless. His people were slain in the Days of the Oppression. The man to whom Our Excellency has awarded the land is, as it were, his maternal uncle."

"Will it come with me and feed the big dogs?" said the Governor.

The other peering children drew back. "Run!" they cried. "Our Excellency will feed Farag to the big dogs."

"I will come," said Farag. 'And I will never go." He threw his arm round Royal's neck, and the wise beast licked his face.

"Binjamin, by Jove!" the Inspector cried.

"No!" said the Governor. "I believe he has the making of James Pigg!"

Farag waved his hand to his uncle, and led Royal on to the barge. The rest of the pack followed.

*   *   *

Gihon, that had seen many sports, learned to know the Hunt barge well. He met her rounding his bends on grey December dawns to music wild and lamentable as the almost forgotten throb of Dervish drums, when, high above Royal's tenor bell, sharper even than lying Beagle-boy's falsetto break, Farag chanted deathless war against Abu Hussein and all his seed. At sunrise the River would shoulder her carefully into her place, and listen to the rush and scutter of the pack fleeing up the gang-plank, and the tramp of the Governor's Arab behind them. They would pass over the brow into the dewless crops, where Gihon, low and shrunken, could only

81

guess what they were about when Abu Hussein flew down the bank to scratch at a stopped earth, and flew back into the barley again. As Farag had foretold, it was evil days for Abu Hussein ere he learned to take the necessary steps and to get away crisply. Sometimes Gihon saw the whole procession of the Hunt silhouetted against the morning blue, bearing him company for many merry miles. At every half mile the horses and donkeys jumped the water-channels – up, on, change your leg, and off again – like figures in a zoetrope, till they grew small along the line of waterwheels. Then Gihon waited their rustling return through the crops, and took them to rest on his bosom at ten o'clock. While the horses ate, and Farag slept with his head on Royal's flank, the Governor and his Inspector worked for the good of the Hunt and his Province.

After a little time there was no need to beat any man for neglecting his earths. The steamer's destination was telegraphed from waterwheel to waterwheel, and the villagers stopped out and put to according. If an earth were overlooked, it meant some dispute as to the ownership of the land, and then and there the Hunt checked and settled it. in this wise: The Governor and the Inspector side by side, but the latter half a horse's length to the rear; both bareshouldered claimants well in front; the villagers half-mooned behind them, and Farag with the pack, who quite understood the performance, sitting down on the left. Twenty minutes were enough to settle the most complicated case, for, as the Governor said to a real Judge on the steamer, "One gets at the truth in a hunting-field a heap quicker than in the law-courts."

"But when the evidence is conflicting?" the Judge suggested.

"Watch the field. They'll throw tongue fast enough if you're running a wrong scent. You've never had an appeal from one of my decisions yet."

The Sheikhs on horseback – the lesser folk on clever donkeys – the children so despised by Farag – soon understood that villages which repaired their waterwheels and channels stood highest in the Governor's favour. He bought their barley for his horses.

82

"Channels," he said, "are necessary that we may all jump them. They are necessary, moreover, for the crops. Let there be many wheels and sound channels – and much good barley."

"Without money," replied an aged Sheikh, "there can be no waterwheels."

"I will lend the money," said the Governor.

"At what interest, O Our Excellency?"

"Take you two of May Queen's puppies to bring up in your village in such a manner that they do not eat filth, nor lose their hair, nor catch fever from lying in the sun, but become wise hounds."

"Like Ray-yal – not like Bigglebai?" (already it was an insult along the River to compare a man to the shifty anthropophagous blue-mottled harrier).

"Certainly, like Ray-yal – not in the least like Bigglebai. *That* shall be the interest on the loan. Let the puppies thrive and the waterwheel be built, and I shall be content," said the Governor.

"The wheel shall be built, but, O Our Excellency, if by God's favour the pups grow to be well-smellers, not filth-eaters, not unaccustomed to their names, not lawless, who will do them and me justice at the time of judging the young dogs?"

"Hounds, man, hounds! Ha-wands, O Sheikh, we call them in their manhood."

"The ha-wands when they are judged at the Sha-ho. I have unfriends down the river to whom Our Excellency has also entrusted ha-wands to bring up."

"Puppies, man! Pah-peaz, we call them O Sheikh, in their childhood."

"Pah-peaz. My enemies may judge my pah-peaz unjustly at the Sha-ho. This must be thought of."

"I see the obstacle. Hear now! If the new waterwheel is built in a month without oppression, thou, O Sheikh, shalt be named one of the judges to judge the pah-peaz at the Sha-ho. It is understood?"

"Understood. We will build the wheel. I and my seed are responsible for the repayment of the loan. Where are my

83

pah-peaz? If they eat fowls, must they on any account eat the feathers?"

"On no account must they eat the feathers. Farag in the barge will tell thee how they are to live."

There is no instance of any default on the Governor's personal and unauthorised loans, for which they called him the Father of Waterwheels. But the first puppy-show at the capital needed enormous tact and the presence of a black battalion ostentatiously drilling in the barrack square to prevent trouble after the prize-giving.

But who can chronicle the glories of the Gihon Hunt – or their shames? Who remembers the kill in the market-place, when the Governor bade the assembled Sheikhs and warriors observe how the hounds would instantly devour the body of Abu Hussein; but how, when he had scientifically broken it up, the weary pack turned from it in loathing, and Farag wept because he said the world's face had been blackened? What men who have not yet ridden beyond the sound of any horn recall the midnight run which ended – Beagleboy leading – among tombs; the hasty whip-off, and the oath, taken above bones, to forget the worry? That desert run, when Abu Hussein forsook the cultivation, and made a six-mile point to earth in a desolate khor – when strange armed riders on camels swooped out of a ravine, and, instead of giving battle, offered to take the tired hounds home on their beasts. Which they did, and vanished.

Above all, who remembers the death of Royal, when a certain Skeikh wept above the body of the stainless hound as it might have been his son's – and that day the Hunt rode no more? The badly kept log-book says little of this, but at the end of their second season (forty-nine brace) appears the dark entry: "New blood badly wanted. They are beginning to listen to Beagle-boy."

*   *   *

The Inspector attended to the matter when his leave fell due.

"Remember," said the Governor, "you must get us the best blood in England – real, dainty hounds – expense

84

no object, but don't trust your own judgment. Present my letters of introduction, and take what they give you."

The Inspector presented his letters in a society where they make much of horses, more of hounds, and are tolerably civil to men who can ride. They passed him from house to house, mounted him according to his merits, and fed him, after five years of goat chop and Worcester sauce, perhaps a thought too richly.

The seat or castle where he made his great coup does not much matter. Four Masters of Foxhounds were at table, and in a mellow hour the Inspector told them stories of the Gihon Hunt. He ended: "Ben said I wasn't to trust my own judgment about hounds; but *I* think there ought to be a special tariff for Empire-makers."

As soon as his hosts could speak, they reassured him on this point.

"And now tell us about your first puppy-show all over again," said one.

"And about the earth-stoppin'. Was that all Ben's own invention?" said another.

"Wait a moment," said a large, clean-shaven man – not an M.F.H. – at the end of the table. "Are your villagers habitually beaten by your Governor when they fail to stop foxes' holes?"

The tone and the phrase were enough, even if, as the Inspector confessed afterwards, the big, blue double-chinned man had not looked so like Beagle-boy. He took him on for the honour of Ethiopia.

"We only hunt twice a week – sometimes three times. I've never known a man chastised more than four times a week – unless there's a bye."

The large loose-lipped man flung his napkin down, came round the table, cast himself into the chair next the Inspector, and leaned forward earnestly, so that he breathed in the Inspector's face.

"Chastised with what?" he said.

"With the *kourbash* – on the feet. A *kourbash* is a strip of old hippo-hide with a sort of keel on it, like the cutting edge of a boar's tusk. But we use the rounded side for a first offender."

85

"And do any consequences follow this sort of thing? For the victim, I mean – not for you?"

"Ve-ry rarely, Let me be fair. I've never seen a man die under the lash, but gangrene may set up if the *kourbash* has been pickled."

"Pickled in what?" All the table was still and interested.

"In copperas, of course. Didn't you know *that*?" said the Inspector.

"Thank God I didn't." The large man spluttered visibly.

The Inspector wiped his face and grew bolder.

"You mustn't think we're careless about our earth-stoppers. We've a Hunt fund for hot tar. Tar's a splendid dressing if the toe-nails aren't beaten off. But huntin' as large a country as we do, we mayn't be back at that village for a month, and if the dressings ain't renewed, and gangrene sets in, often as not you find your man pegging about on his stumps. We've a well-known local name for 'em down the river. We call 'em the Mudir's Cranes. You see, I persuaded the Governor to bastinado only on one foot.'

"On one foot? The Mudir's Cranes!" The large man turned purple to the top of his bald head. 'Would you mind giving me the local word for Mudir's Cranes?"

From a too well stocked memory the Inspector drew one short adhesive word which surprises by itself even un-blushing Ethiopia. He spelt it out, saw the large man write it down on his cuff and withdraw. Then the Inspector trans-lated a few of its significations and implications to the four Masters of Foxhounds. He left three days later with eight couple of the best hounds in England – a free and a friendly and an ample gift from four packs to the Gihon Hunt. He had honestly meant to undeceive the large blue-mottled man, but somehow forgot about it.

The new draft marks a new chapter in the Hunt's history. From an isolated phenomenon in a barge it became a perma-nent institution with brick-built kennels ashore, and an in-fluence, social, political, and administrative, coterminous with the boundaries of the Province. Ben, the Governor, de-parted to England, where he kept a pack of real dainty hounds, but never ceased to long for the old lawless lot. His successors were *ex-officio* Masters of the Gihon Hunt, as all Inspectors were Whips. For one reason, Farag, the kennel-huntsman, in khaki and puttees, would obey nothing under the rank of an Excellency, and the hounds would obey no one but Farag; for another, the best way of estimating crop returns and revenue was by riding straight to hounds; for a third, though Judges down the river issued signed and sealed land-titles to all lawful owners, yet public opinion along the river never held any such title valid till it had been con-firmed, according to precedent, by the Governor's hunting-crop in the hunting-field, above the wilfully neglected earth. True, the ceremony had been cut down to three mere taps on the shoulder, but Governors who tried to evade that much found themselves and their office compassed about with a great cloud of witnesses who took up their time with lawsuits and, worse still, neglected the puppies. The older Sheikhs, indeed, stood out for the immeasurable beatings of the old days – the sharper the punishment, they argued, the surer the title; but here the hand of modern progress was against them, and they contented themselves with telling tales of Ben the first Governor, whom they called the Father of Waterwheels, and of that heroic age when men, horses, and hounds were worth following.

This same Modern Progress which brought dog-biscuit and brass water-taps to the kennels was at work all over the world. Forces, Activities, and Movements sprang into being, agitated themselves, coalesced, and, in one political avalanche, overwhelmed a bewildered, and not in the least intending it, England. The echoes of the New Era were borne into the Province on the wings of inexplicable cables. The Gihon Hunt read speeches and sentiments and policies which amazed them, and they thanked God, prematurely, that their Province was too far off, too hot, and too hard-worked to be reached by those speakers or their policies. But they, with the others, underestimated the scope and purpose of the New Era.

One by one the Provinces of the Empire were hauled up and baited, hit and held, lashed under the belly, and forced back on their haunches for the amusement of their new masters in the parish of Westminster. One by one they fell away, sore and angry, to compare stripes with each other at the ends of the uneasy earth. Even so the Gihon Hunt, like Abu Hussein in the old days, did not understand. Then it reached them through the Press that they habitually flogged to death good revenue-paying cultivators who neglected to stop earths; but that the few, the very few, who did not die under hippo-hide whips soaked in copperas, walked about on their gangrenous ankle-bones, and were known in derision as the Mudir's Cranes. The charges were vouched for in the House of Commons by a Mr. Lethabie Groombride, who had formed a Committee, and was disseminating literature. The Province groaned; the Inspector – now an Inspector of Inspectors – whistled. He had forgotten the gentleman who sputtered in people's faces.

"He shouldn't have looked so like Beagle-boy!" was his sole defence when he met the Governor at breakfast on the steamer after a meet.

"You shouldn't have joked with an animal of that class," said Peter the Governor. "Look what Farag has brought me!"

It was a pamphlet, signed on behalf of a Committee by a lady secretary, but composed by some person who thoroughly understood the language of the Province. After telling the tale of the beatings, it recommended all the beaten to institute criminal proceedings against their Governor, and, as soon as might be, to rise against English oppression and tyranny. Such documents were new in Ethiopia in those days.

The Inspector read the last half-page. "But – but," he stammered, "this is impossible. White men don't write this sort of stuff."

"Don't they, just?" said the Governor. "They get made Cabinet Ministers for doing it too. I went home last year, I know."

"It'll blow over," said the Inspector weakly.

"Not it. Groombride is coming down here to investigate the matter in a few days."

"For himself?"

"The Imperial Government's behind him. Perhaps you'd

like to look at my orders." The Governor laid down an un-coded cable. The whiplash to it ran: "You will afford Mr. Groombride every facility for his inquiry, and will be held responsible that no obstacles are put in his way to the fullest possible examination of any witnesses which he may consider necessary. He will be accompanied by his own interpreter, who must not be tampered with."

"That's to me – Governor of the Province!" said Peter the Governor.

"It seems about enough," the Inspector answered.

Farag, kennel-huntsman, entered the saloon, as was his privilege.

"My uncle, who was beaten by the Father of Waterwheels, would approach, O Excellency," he said, "and there are also others on the bank."

"Admit," said the Governor.

There tramped aboard Sheikhs and villagers to the number of seventeen. In each man's hand was a copy of the pamphlet; in each man's eye terror and uneasiness of the sort that Governors spend and are spent to clear away. Farag's uncle, now Sheikh of the village, spoke: "It is written in this book, O Excellency, that the beatings whereby we hold our lands are all valueless. It is written that every man who received such a beating from the Father of Waterwheels who slew the Emirs should instantly begin a lawsuit, because the title to his land is not valid."

"It is so written. We do not wish lawsuits. We wish to hold our land as it was given to us after the Days of the Oppression," they cried all together.

The Governor glanced at the Inspector. This was serious. To cast doubt on the ownership of land means, in Ethiopia, the letting in of waters, and the getting out of troops.

"Your titles are good," said the Governor. The Inspector confirmed with a nod.

"Then what is the meaning of these writings which come from down the river where the Judges are?" Farag's uncle waved his copy. "By whose order are we ordered to slay *you*, O Excellency Our Governor?"

"It is not written that you are to slay me."

"Not in those very words, but if we leave an earth un-stopped, it is the same as though we wished to save Abu Hussein from the hounds. These writings say: 'Abolish the rulers.' How can we abolish except we kill? We hear rumours of one who comes from down the river soon to lead us to kill."

"Fools!" said the Governor. "Your titles are good. This is madness!"

"It is so written," they answered like a pack.

"Listen," said the Inspector smoothly. "I know who caused the writings to be written and sent. He is a man of a blue-mottled jowl, in aspect like Bigglebai who ate unclean matters. He will come up the river and will give tongue about the beatings."

"Will he impeach our land-titles? An evil day for him!"

"Go slow, Baker," the Governor whispered. "They'll kill him if they get scared about their land."

"I tell a parable." The Inspector lit a cigarette. "Declare which of you took to walk the children of Milkmaid?"

"Melik-meid First or Second?" said Farag quickly.

"The second – the one which was lamed by the thorn."

"No – no. Melik-meid the Second strained her shoulder leaping my water-channel," a Sheikh cried. "Melik-meid the First was lamed by the thorns on the day Our Excellency fell thrice."

"True – true. The second Melik-meid's mate was Malvolio, the pied hound," said the Inspector.

"I had two of the second Melik-meid's pups," said Farag's uncle. "They died of the madness in their ninth month."

"And how did they do before they died?" said the Inspector.

"They ran about in the sun and slavered at the mouth till they died."

"Wherefore?"

"God knows. He sent the madness. It was no fault of mine."

"Thine own mouth hath answered thee," the Inspector laughed. 'It is with men as it is with dogs. God afflicts some with a madness. It is no fault of ours if such men run about in the sun and froth at the mouth. The man who is coming will emit spray from his mouth in speaking, and will always edge and push in towards his hearers. When ye see and hear him ye will understand that he is afflicted of God: being mad. He is in God's Hand."

"But our titles! Are our titles to our lands good?" the crowd repeated.

"Your titles are in my hands – they are good," said the Governor.

"And he who wrote the writings is an afflicted of God?" said Farag's uncle.

"The Inspector hath said it," cried the Governor. "Ye will see when the man comes. O Sheikhs and men, have we ridden together and walked puppies together, and bought and sold barley for the horses, that, after these years, we should run riot on the scent of a madman – an afflicted of God?"

"But the Hunt pays us to kill mad jackals," said Farag's uncle. "And he who questions my titles to my land –"

"Aahh! 'Ware riot!" The Governor's hunting-crop cracked like a three-pounder. "By Allah," he thundered, "if the afflicted of God comes to any harm at your hands, I myself will shoot every hound and every puppy, and the Hunt shall ride no more. On your heads be it. Go in peace, and tell the others."

"The Hunt shall ride no more?" said Farag's uncle. "Then how can the land be governed? No – no, O Excellency Our Governor, we will not harm a hair on the head of the afflicted of God. He shall be to us as is Abu Hussein's wife in her breeding season."

When they were gone the Governor mopped his forehead.

"We must put a few soldiers in every village this Groombride visits, Baker. Tell 'em to keep out of sight, and have an eye on the villagers. He's trying 'em rather high."

"O Excellency," said the smooth voice of Farag, laying *The Field* and *Country Life* square on the table, "is the afflicted of God who resembles Bigglebai one with the man whom the Inspector met in the great house in England, and to whom he told the tale of the Mudir's Cranes?"

"The same man, Farag," said the Inspector.

91

"I have often heard the Inspector tell the tale to Our Excellency at feeding-time in the kennels; but since I am in the Government service I have never told it to my people. May I loose that tale among the villages?"

The Governor nodded. "No harm," he said.

*   *   *

The details of Mr. Groombride's arrival, with his interpreter, who, he proposed, should eat with him at the Governor's table, his allocution to the Governor on the New Movement and the sins of Imperialism, I purposely omit. At three in the afternoon Mr. Groombride said: "I will go out now and address your victims in this village."

"Won't you find it rather hot?" said the Governor. "They generally take a nap till sunset at this time of year."

Mr. Groombride's large, loose lips set. "*That,*" he replied pointedly, "would be enough to decide me. I fear you have not quite mastered your instructions. May I ask you to send for my interpreter? I hope he has not been tampered with by your subordinates."

He was a yellowish boy called Abdul, who had well eaten and drunk with Farag. The Inspector, by the way, was not present at the meal.

"At whatever risk, I shall go unattended," said Mr. Groombridge. "Your presence would cow them from giving evidence. Abdul, my good friend, would you very kindly open the umbrella?"

He passed up the gang-plank to the village, and with no more prelude than a Salvation Army picket in a Portsmouth slum, cried: "Oh, my brothers!"

He did not guess how his path had been prepared. The village was widely awake. Farag, in loose, flowing garments, quite unlike a kennel-huntsman's khaki and puttees, leaned against the wall of his uncle's house. 'Come and see the afflicted of God," he cried musically, "whose face, indeed, resembles that of Bigglebai."

The village came, and decided that on the whole Farag was right.

92

"I can't quite catch what they are saying," said Mr. Groombride.

"They saying they very much pleased to see you, sar," Abdul interpreted.

"Then I do think they might have sent a deputation to the steamer; but I suppose they were frightened of the officials. Tell them not to be frightened, Abdul."

"He says you are not to be frightened," Abdul explained. A child here sputtered with laughter. 'Refrain from mirth," Farag cried. "The afflicted of God is the guest of The Excellency Our Governor. We are responsible for every hair of his head."

"He has none," a voice spoke. "He has the white and the shining mange."

"Now tell them what I have come for, Abdul, and please keep the umbrella well up. I think I shall reserve myself for my little vernacular speech at the end."

"Approach! Look! Listen!" Abdul chanted. "The afflicted of God will now make sport. Presently he will speak in your tongue, and will consume you with mirth. I have been his servant for three weeks. I will tell you about his undergarments and his perfumes for his head."

He told them at length.

"And didst thou take any of his perfume bottles?" said Farag at the end.

"I am his servant. I took two," Abdul replied.

"Ask him," said Farag's uncle, "what he knows about our land-titles. Ye young men are all alike." He waved a pamphlet. Mr. Groombride smiled to see how the seed sown in London had borne fruit by Gihon. Lo, all the seniors held copies of the pamphlet!

"He knows less than a buffalo. He told me on the steamer that he was driven out of his own land by Demah-Kerazi, which is a devil inhabiting crowds and assemblies," said Abdul.

"Allah between us and Evil!" a woman cackled from the darkness of a hut. "Come in, children, he may have the Evil Eye."

"No, my aunt," said Farag. "No afflicted of God has an

evil eye. Wait till you hear his mirth-provoking speech which he will deliver. I have heard it twice from Abdul."

"They seem very quick to grasp the point. How far have you got, Abdul?"

"All about the beatings, sar. They are highly interested."

"Don't forget about the local self-government, and please hold the umbrella over me. It is hopeless to destroy unless one first builds up."

"He may not have the Evil Eye," Farag's uncle grunted, "but his devil led him too certainly to question my land-title. Ask him whether he still doubts my land-title?"

"Or mine, or mine?" cried the elders.

"What odds? He is an afflicted of God," Farag called. "Remember the tale I told you."

"Yes, but he is an Englishman, and doubtless of influence, or Our Excellency would not entertain him. Bid that down-country jackass ask him."

"Sar," said Abdul, "these people much fearing they may be turned out of their land in consequence of your remarks. Therefore they ask you to make promise no bad consequences following your visit."

Mr. Groombride held his breath and turned purple. Then he stamped his foot.

"Tell them," he cried, "that if a hair of any one of their heads is touched by any official on any account whatever, all England shall ring with it. Good God! What callous oppression! The dark places of the earth are full of cruelty." He wiped his face, and throwing out his arms cried: "Tell them, oh! tell the poor serfs not to be afraid of me. Tell them I come to redress their wrongs – not, Heaven knows, to add to their burden."

The long-drawn gurgle of the practised public speaker pleased them much.

"That is how the new water-tap runs out in the kennel," said Farag. "The Excellency Our Governor entertains him that he may make much sport. Make him say the mirth-moving speach."

"What did he say about my land-titles?" Farag's uncle was not to be turned.

"He says," Farag interpreted, "that he desires nothing

94

better than that you should live on your lands in peace. He talks as though he believed himself to be Governor."

"Well. We here are all witnesses to what he has said. Now go forward with the sport." Farag's uncle smoothed his garments. "How diversely hath Allah made His creatures! On one He bestows strength to slay Emirs. Another He causes to go mad and wander in the sun, like the afflicted sons of Melik-meid."

"Yes, and to emit spray from the mouth, as the Inspector told us. All will happen as the Inspector foretold," said Farag. "I have never yet seen the Inspector thrown out during any run."

"I think," – Abdul plucked at Mr. Groombride's sleeves, – "I think perhaps it is better now, sar, if you give your fine little native speech. They not understanding English, but much pleased at your condescensions."

"Condescensions?" Mr. Groombride spun round. "If they only knew how I felt towards them in my heart! If I could express a tithe of my feelings! I must stay here and learn the language. Hold up the umbrella, Abdul! I think my little speech will show them I know something of their *vie intime.*"

It was a short, simple, carefully-learned address, and the accent, supervised by Abdul on the steamer, allowed the hearers to guess its meaning, which was a request to see one of the Mudir's Cranes; since the desire of the speaker's life, the object to which he would consecrate his days, was to improve the condition of the Mudir's Cranes. But first he must behold them with his own eyes. Would, then, his brethren, whom he loved, show him a Mudir's Crane whom he desired to love?"

Once, twice, and again in his peroration he repeated his demand, using always – that they might see he was acquainted with their local argot – using always, I say, the word which the Inspector had given him in England long ago – the short adhesive word which, by itself, surprises even unblushing Ethiopia.

There are limits to the sublime politeness of an ancient people. A bulky, blue-chinned man in white clothes, his

95

name red-lettered across his lower shirt-front, spluttering from under a green-lined umbrella almost tearful appeals to be introduced to the Unintroducible; naming loudly the Unnameable; dancing, as it seemed, in perverse joy at mere mention of the Unmentionable – found those limits. There was a moment's hush, and then such mirth as Gihon through his centuries had never heard – a roar like to the roar of his own cataracts in flood. Children cast themselves on the ground, and rolled back and forth cheering and whooping; strong men, their faces hidden in their clothes, swayed in silence, till the agony became insupportable, and they threw up their heads and bayed at the sun; women, mothers and virgins, shrilled shriek upon mounting shriek, and slapped their thighs as it might have been the roll of musketry. When they tried to draw breath, some half-strangled voice would quack out the word, and the riot began afresh. Last to fall was the city-trained Abdul. He held on to the edge of apoplexy, then collapsed, throwing the umbrella from him.

Mr. Groombride should not be judged too harshly. Exercise and strong emotion under a hot sun, the shock of public ingratitude, for the moment ruffled his spirit. He furled the umbrella, and with it beat the prostrate Abdul, crying that he had been betrayed.

In which posture the Inspector, on horseback, followed by the Governor, suddenly found him.

*   *   *

"That's all very well," said the Inspector, when he had taken Abdul's dramatically dying depositions on the steamer, "but you can't hammer a native merely because he laughs at you. I see nothing for it but for the law to take its course."

"You might reduce the charge to – er – tampering with an interpreter," said the Governor. Mr. Groombride was too far gone to be comforted.

"It's the publicity that I fear," he wailed. "Is there no possible means of hushing up the affair? You don't know what a question – a single question in the House means to a man in my position – the ruin of my political career, I assure you."

"I shouldn't have imagined it," said the Governor thoughtfully.

"And, though perhaps I ought not to say it, I am not without honour in my own country – or influence. A word in season, as you know, Your Excellency. It might carry an official far."

The Governor shuddered.

"Yes, *that* had to come too," he said to himself. "Well, look here. If I tell this man of yours to withdraw the charge against you, you can go to Gehenna for aught I care. The only condition I make is, that if you write – I supose that's part of your business – about your travels, you don't praise *me!*"

So far Mr. Groombride has loyally adhered to this understanding.

7

★ THE HORSE MARINES
★ THE CENTAURS

Kipling never lost his fascination for the army and military matters in particular those concerned with the mounted arm which held his interest always. Take, for instance, *The Jacket* (Horse Artillery) *Snarleyyow* (Field Gunners) and M.I. (Mounted Infantry), with its well-known lines:

> "We don't 'old on by the mane no more, nor
>   Lose our stirrups – much.
> That is what we are known as – we are
>   The beggars that got
> Three days to learn equitation, an' six months o' bloomin'
>   Well trot!"

Nor did he forget those cavalry subalterns he had known in India and admired for their dash and courage in riding over fences or in front of their Regiments when they.

> "Went slap for the Gahzi, my sword at my side,
>   When we rode hell for leather
>   Both squadrons together,
> That didn't care whether we lived or we died."

The subalterns had talked to him about the toughness of the riding school at Sandhurst and, after they had joined their regiments, the hoops they had been put through by the rough riders there. When Kipling read the newspaper quotation he has put at the head of this story he hooted derisively, sat down and wrote *The Horse Marines*.

Kipling is in his best comic vein when untainted by the spleen or vindictiveness that runs through others of his funnies notably the famous *Village That Voted The Earth Was Flat*. The punch line at the end, unusual in his work, is a beauty.

And so this would appear to be the appropriate place to append his hymn to the cavalry:

CAVALRY HORSES.

By the brand on my withers, the finest of tunes
Is played by the Lancers, Hussars, and Dragoons,
And it's sweeter than "Stables" or "Water" to me
The Cavalry Canter of "Bonnie Dundee!"

Then feed us and break us and handle and groom,
And give us good riders and plenty of room,
And launch us in column of squadron and see
The way of the War-horse to "Bonnie Dundee!"

THE HORSE MARINES

The Rt. Hon. R. B. Haldane, Secretary of State for War, was questioned in the House of Commons on April 8th about the rocking-horses which the War Office is using for the purpose of teaching recruits to ride. Lord Ronaldshay asked the War Secretary if rocking-horses were to be supplied to all the cavalry regiments for teaching recruits to ride. "The noble Lord," replied Mr. Haldane, "is doubtless alluding to certain dummy horses on rockers which have been tested with very satisfactory results." . . . The mechanical steed is a wooden horse with an astonishing tail. It is painted brown and mounted on swinging rails. The recruit leaps into the saddle and pulls at the reins while the riding-instructor rocks the animal to and fro with his foot. The rocking-horses are being made at Woolwich. They are quite cheap.

Daily Paper

My instructions to Mr. Leggatt, my engineer, had been accurately obeyed. He was to bring my car on completion of annual overhaul, from Coventry *via* London, to Southampton Docks to await my arrival; and very pretty she looked, under the steamer's side among the railway lines, at six in the morning. Next to her new paint and varnish I was most impressed by her four brand-new tyres.

"But I didn't order new tyres," I said as we moved away. "These are Irresilients, too."

"Treble-ribbed," said Leggatt. "Diamond-stud sheathing."

"Then there has been a mistake."

"Oh no, sir; they're gratis."

The number of motor manufacturers who give away complete sets of treble-ribbed Irresilient tyres is so limited that I believe I asked Leggatt for an explanation.

"I don't know that I could very well explain, sir," was the answer. "It 'ud come better from Mr. Pyecroft. He's on leaf at Portsmouth – staying with his uncle. His uncle 'ad the body all night. I'd defy you to find a scratch on her even with a microscope."

"Then we will go home by the Portsmouth road," I said.

And we went at those speeds which are allowed before the working-day begins or the police are thawed out. We were blocked near Portsmouth by a battalion of Regulars on the move.

"Whitsuntide manœuvres just ending," said Leggatt. "They've had a fortnight in the Downs."

He said no more until we were in a narrow street somewhere behind Portsmouth Town Railway Station, where he slowed at a green-grocery shop. The door was open, and a small old man sat on three potato-baskets swinging his feet over a stooping blue back.

"You call that shinin' 'em?" he piped. "Can you see your face in 'em yet? No! Then shine 'em, or I'll give you a beltin' you'll remember!"

"If you stop kickin' me in the mouth perhaps I'd do better," said Pyecroft's voice meekly.

100

We blew the horn.

Pyecroft arose, put away the brushes, and received us not otherwise than as a king in his own country.

"Are you going to leave me up here all day?" said the old man.

Pyecroft lifted him down and he hobbled into the back room.

"It's his corns," Pyecroft explained. "You can't shine corny feet – and he hasn't had his breakfast."

"I haven't had mine either," I said.

"Breakfast for two more, uncle," Pyecroft sang out.

"Go out an' buy it then," was the answer, "or else it's half-rations."

Pyecroft turned to Leggatt, gave him his marketing orders, and despatched him with the coppers.

"I have got four new tyres on my car," I began impressively.

"Yes," said Mr. Pyecroft. "You have, and I *will* say" – he patted my car's bonnet – "you earned 'em."

"I want to know why – ," I went on.

"Quite justifiable. You haven't noticed anything in the papers, have you?"

"I've only just landed. I haven't seen a paper for weeks."

"Then you can lend me a virgin ear. There's been a scandal in the Junior Service – the Army, I believe they call 'em."

A bag of coffee-beans pitched on the counter. "Roast that," said the uncle from within.

Pyecroft rigged a small coffee-roaster, while I took down the shutters, and sold a young lady in curl-papers two bunches of mixed greens and one soft orange.

"Sickly stuff to handle on an empty stomach, ain't it?" said Pyecroft.

"What about my new tyres?" I insisted.

"Oh, any amount. But the question is" – he looked at me steadily – "is this what you might call a court-martial or a post-mortem inquiry?"

"Strictly a post-mortem," said I.

"That being so," said Pyecroft, "we can rapidly arrive at facts. Last Thursday – the shutters go behind those baskets – last Thursday at five bells in the forenoon watch, otherwise ten-thirty a.m., your Mr. Leggatt was discovered on West-minster Bridge laying his course for the Old Kent Road."

"But that doesn't lead to Southampton," I interrupted.

"Then perhaps he was swinging the car for compasses. Be that as it may, we found him in that latitude, simultaneous as Jules and me was *ong route* for Waterloo to rejoin our respect-ive ships – or Navies I should say. Jules was a *permissionaire*, which meant being on leaf, same as me, from a French cassowary-cruiser at Portsmouth. A party of her trusty and well-beloved petty officers 'ad been seeing London, chaper-oned by the R.C. chaplain. Jules 'ad detached himself from the squadron and was cruisin' on his own when I joined him, in company of copious lady-friends. *But*, mark you, your Mr. Leggatt drew the line at the girls. Loud and long he drew it."

"I'm glad of that," I said.

"You may be. He adopted the puristical formation from the first. 'Yes,' he said, when we was annealing him at – but you wouldn't know the pub – 'I *am* going to Southampton,' he says, 'and I'll stretch a point to go *via* Portsmouth; *but*,' says he, 'seeing what sort of one hell of a time invariably trarnspires when we cruise together, Mr. Pyecroft, I do *not* feel myself justified towards my generous and long-suffering employer in takin' on that kind of ballast as well.' I assure you he considered your interests."

"And the girls?" I asked.

"Oh, I left that to Jules. I'm a monogomite by nature. So we embarked strictly *ong garçong*. But I should tell you, in case he didn't, that your Mr. Leggatt's care for your interests 'ad extended to sheathing the car in matting and gunny-bags to preserve her paint-work. She was all swathed up like an I-talian baby."

"He *is* careful about his paint-work," I said.

"For a man with no Service experience I should say he was fair homicidal on the subject. If we'd been Marines he couldn't have been more pointed in his allusions to our hob-nailed socks. However, we reduced him to a malleable con-dition, and embarked for Portsmouth. I'd seldom rejoined my *vaisseau ong automobile*, *avec* a fur coat and goggles. Nor 'ad Jules."

"Did Jules say much?" I asked, helplessly turning the handle of the coffee-roaster.

"That's where I pitied the pore beggar. He 'adn't the language, so to speak. He was confined to heavings and shruggin's and copious *Mong Jews*! The French are very badly fitted with relief-valves. And then our Mr. Leggatt drove. He drove."

"Was he in a very malleable condition?"

"Not him! We recognised the value of his cargo from the outset. He hadn't a chance to get more than moist at the edges. After which we went to sleep; and now we'll go to breakfast."

We entered the back room where everything was in order, and a screeching canary made us welcome. The uncle had added sausages and piles of buttered toast to the kippers. The coffee, cleared with a piece of fish-skin, was a revelation.

Leggatt, who seemed to know the premises, had run the car into the tiny backyard where her mirror-like back almost blocked up the windows. He minded shop while we ate. Pyecroft passed him his rations through a flap in the door. The uncle ordered him in, after breakfast, to wash up, and he jumped in his gaiters at the old man's commands as he had never jumped to mine.

"To resoom the post-mortem," said Pyecroft, lighting his pipe. "My slumbers were broken by the propeller ceasing to revolve, and by vile language from your Mr. Leggatt."

'I – I – " Leggatt began, a blue-checked duster in one hand and a cup in the other.

"When you're wanted aft you'll be sent for, Mr. Leggatt," said Pyecroft amiably. "It's clean mess decks for you now. Resooming once more, we was on a lonely and desolate ocean near Portsdown, surrounded by gorse bushes, and a Boy Scout was stirring my stomach with his little copper-stick."

" 'You count ten,' he says.

" 'Very good, Boy Jones,' I says, 'count 'em,' and I hauled him in over the gunnel, and ten I gave him with my large flat hand. The remarks he passed, lying face down tryin' to bite my leg, would have reflected credit on any Service. Having finished I dropped him overboard again, which was my gross political error. I ought to 'ave killed him; because he began signalling – rapid and accurate – in a sou' westerly direction. Few equatorial calms are to be apprehended when B.P.'s little pets take to signallin'. Make a note o' that! Three minutes later we were stopped and boarded by Scouts – up our backs, down our necks, and in our boots! The last I heard from your Mr. Leggatt as he went under, brushin' 'em off his cap, was thanking Heaven he'd covered up the new paint-work with mats. An 'eroic soul!"

"Not a scratch on her body," said Leggatt, pouring out the coffee-grounds.

"And Jules?" said I.

"Oh, Jules thought the much advertised Social Revolution had begun, but his mackintosh hampered him."

"You told me to bring the mackintosh," Leggatt whispered to me.

"And when I 'ad 'em half convinced he was a French vicomte coming down to visit the Commander-in-Chief at Portsmouth, he tried to take it off. Seeing his uniform under-neath, some sucking Sherlock Holmes of the Pink Eye Patrol (they called him Eddy) deduced that I wasn't telling the truth. Eddy said I was tryin' to sneak into Portsmouth un-observed – unobserved mark you! – and join hands with the enemy. It trarnspired that the Scouts was conducting a field-day against opposin' forces, ably assisted by all branches of the Service, and they were so afraid the car wouldn't count ten points to them in the fray, that they'd have scalped us, but for the intervention of an umpire – also in short under-drawers. A fleshy sight!"

Here Mr. Pyecroft shut his eyes and nodded. "That umpire," he said suddenly, "was our Mr. Morshed – a gentleman whose acquaintance you have already made *and* profited by, if I mistake not.'

"Oh, was the Navy in it too?" I said; for I had read of wild doings occasionally among the Boy Scouts on the Ports-mouth Road, in which Navy, Army, and the world at large seemed to have taken part.

"The Navy *was* in it. I was the only one out of it – for several seconds. Our Mr. Morshed failed to recognise me in my fur boa, and my appealin' winks at 'im behind your goggles didn't arrive. But when Eddy darling had told his story, I saluted, which is difficult in furs, and I stated I was bringin' him dispatches from the North. My Mr. Morshed cohered on the instant. I've never known his ethergram installations out of order yet. "Go and guard your blessed road," he says to the Fratton Orphan Asylum standing at attention all round him, and, when they was removed – "Pyecroft," he says, still *sotte voce*, "what in Hong-Kong are you doing with this dun-coloured *sampan*?"

"It was your Mr. Leggatt's paint-protective matting which caught his eye. She *did* resemble a *sampan*, especially about the stern-works. At these remarks I naturally threw myself on 'is bosom, so far as Service conditions permitted, and revealed him all, mentioning that the car was yours. You know his way of working his lips like a rabbit? Yes, he was quite pleased. "*His* car!" he kept murmuring, working his lips like a rabbit. "I owe 'im more than a trifle for things he wrote about me. I'll keep the car."

"Your Mr. Leggatt now injected some semimutinous remarks to the effect that he was your chauffeur in charge of your car, and, as such, capable of so acting. Mr. Morshed threw him a glance. It sufficed. Didn't it suffice, Mr. Leggatt?"

"I knew if something didn't happen, something worse would," said Leggatt. "It never fails when you're aboard."

"And Jules?" I demanded.

"Jules was, so to speak, panicking in a water-tight flat through his unfortunate lack of language. I had to introduce him as part of the *entente cordiale*, and he was put under arrest, too. Then we sat on the grass and smoked, while Eddy and Co. violently annoyed the traffic on the Portsmouth Road, till the umpires, all in short panties, conferred on the valuable lessons of the field-day and added up points, same as at target-practice. I didn't hear their conclusions, but our Mr. Morshed delivered a farewell address to Eddy and Co., tellin' 'em they ought to have deduced from a hundred signs about me, that I was a friendly bringin' in dispatches from the North. We left 'em tryin' to find those signs in the Scout book, and we reached Mr. Morshed's hotel at Portsmouth at 6.27 pm *ong automobile*. Here endeth the first chapter."

"Begin the second," I said.

The uncle and Leggatt had finished washing up and were seated, smoking, while the damp duster dried at the fire.

"About what time was it," said Pyecroft to Leggatt, 'when our Mr. Morshed began to talk about uncles?"

"When he came back to the bar, after he'd changed into those rat-catcher clothes," said Leggatt.

"That's right. 'Pye,' said he, 'have you an uncle?' 'I have,' I says. 'Here's santy to him,' and I finished my sherry and bitters to *you*, uncle."

"That's right," said Pyecroft's uncle sternly. "If you hadn't I'd have belted you worth rememberin', Emmanuel. I had the body all night."

Pyecroft smiled affectionately. "So you 'ad, uncle," an' beautifully you looked after her. But as I was saying, 'I have an uncle, too,' says Mr. Morshed, dark and lowering. 'Yet somehow I can't love him. I was to mortify the beggar. Volunteers to mortify my uncle, one pace to the front.'

"I took Jules with me the regulation distance. Jules was getting interested. Your Mr. Leggatt preserved a strictly nootral attitude.

"'You're a pressed man,' says our Mr. Morshed. 'I owe your late employer much, so to say. The car will manœuvre all right, as requisite.'

"Mr. Leggatt come out noble as your employee, and, by 'Eaven's divine grace, instead of arguing, he pleaded his new paint and varnish which was Mr. Morshed's one vital spot (he's lootenant on one of the new catch-'em-alive-o's now). 'True,' says he, 'paint's an 'oly thing. I'll give you one hour to arrange a *modus vivendi*. Full bunkers and steam ready by 9 p.m. to-night, *if* you please.'

"Even so, Mr. Leggatt was far from content, I'ad to arrange the details. We run her into the yard here." Pyecroft nodded through the window at my car's glossy back-panels. "We took off the body with its mats and put it in the stable, substitooting (and that yard's a tight fit for extensive repairs) the body of uncle's blue delivery cart. It overhung a trifle, but

106

after I'd lashed it I knew it wouldn't fetch loose. Thus, in our composite cruiser, we repaired once more to the hotel, and was immediately dispatched to the toy-shop in the High Street where we took aboard one rocking-horse which was waiting for us."

"Took aboard *what*?" I cried.

"One fourteen-hand dapple-grey rocking-horse, with pure green rockers and detachable tail, pair gashly glass eyes, complete set 'orrible grinnin' teeth, and two bloody-red nostrils which, protruding from the brown papers, produced the *tout ensemble* of a Ju-ju sacrifice in the Benin campaign. Do I make myself comprehensible?"

"Perfectly. Did you say anything?" I asked.

"Only to Jules. To him, as I says, wishing to try him, '*Allez à votre bateau. Je say mon Lootenoug. Eel voo donneray porkwor.*' To me, says he, '*Vous ong ate hurroo! Jamay de la vee!*' and I saw by his eye he'd taken on for the full term of the war. Jules was a blue-eyed, brindle-haired beggar of a useful make and inquirin' habits. Your Mr. Leggat he only groaned."

Leggatt nodded. "It was like nightmares," he said. "It was like nightmares."

"Once more, then," Pyecroft swept on, "we returned to the hotel and partook of a sumptuous repast, under the able and genial chairmanship of our Mr. Morshed, who laid his projecks unreservedly before us. 'In the first place,' he says, opening out bicycle-maps, 'my uncle, who, I regret to say, is a brigadier-general, has sold his alleged soul to Dicky Bridoon for a feathery hat and a pair o' gilt spurs. Jules, *conspuez l'oncle!*' So Jules, you'll be glad to hear – "

"One minute, Pye," I said, "Who is Dicky Bridoon?"

"I don't usually mingle myself up with the bickerings of the Junior Service, but it trarnspired that he was Secretary o' State for Civil War, an' he'd been issuing mechanical leather-belly gee-gees which doctors recommend for tumour – to the British cavalry in loo of real meat horses, to learn to ride on. Don't you remember there was quite a stir in the papers owing to the cavalry not appreciatin' 'em? But that's a minor item. The main point was that our uncle, in his capacity of brigadier-general, mark you, had wrote to the papers highly approvin' o' Dicky Bridoon's mechanical substitutes an 'ad thus obtained promotion – all same as a agnosticle stoker psalm-singin' 'imself up the Service under a pious captain. At that point of the narrative we caught a phosphorescent glimmer why the rocking-horse might have been issued; but none the less the navigation was intricate. Omitting the fact it was dark and cloudy, our brigadier-uncle lay somewhere in the South Downs with his brigade, which was manœuvrin' at Whitsun manœuvres on a large scale – Red Army *versus* Blue, et cetera; an' all we 'ad to go by was those flapping bicycle-maps and your Mr. Leggatt's groans."

"I was thinking what the Downs mean after dark," said Leggatt angrily.

"They was worth thinkin' of," said Pyecroft. "When we had studied the map till it fair spun, we decided to sally forth and creep for uncle by hand in the dark, dark night, an' present 'im with the rocking-horse. So we embarked at 8.57 p.m."

"One minute again, please. How much did Jules understand by that time?" I asked.

"Sufficient unto the day – or night, perhaps I should say. He told Our Mr. Morshed he'd follow him *more sang frays*, which is French for dead, drunk or damned. Barrin' 'is paucity o' language, there wasn't a blemish on Jules. But what I wished to imply was, when we climbed into the back parts of the car, our Lootenant Morshed says to me, 'I doubt if I'd flick my cigar-ends about too lavish, Mr. Pyecroft. We ought to be sitting on five pounds' worth of selected fireworks, and I think the rockets are your end.' Not being able to smoke with my 'ead over the side I threw it away; and then your Mr. Leggatt, 'having been as nearly mutinous as it pays to be with my Mr. Morshed, arched his back and drove."

"Where did he drive to, please?" said I.

"Primerrily, in search of any or either or both armies; seconderrily, of course, in search of our brigadier-uncle. Not finding him on the road, we ran about the grass looking for him. This took us to a great many places in a short time. 'Ow 'eavenly that lilac did smell on top of that first Down – stinkin' its blossomin' little heart out!"

108

"I 'adn't leesure to notice," said Mr. Leggatt. "The Downs were full o' chalk-pits, and we'd no lights."

"We 'ad the bicycle-lamp to look at the map by. Didn't you notice the old lady at the window where we saw the man in the night-gown? I thought night-gowns as sleepin' rig was extinck, so to speak."

"I tell you I 'adn't leesure to notice," Leggatt repeated.

"That's odd. Then what might 'ave made you tell the sentry at the first camp we found that you was the *Daily Express* delivery-waggon?"

"You can't touch pitch without being defiled," Leggatt answered. " 'Oo told the officer in the bath we were umpires?"

"Well, he asked us. That was when we found the Territorial battalion undressin' in slow time. It lay on the left flank o' the Blue Army, and it cackled as it lay, too. But it gave us our position as regards the respective armies. We wandered a little more, and at 11.7 p.m., not having had a road under us for twenty minutes, we scaled the heights of something or other – which are about six hundred feet high. Here we 'alted to tighten the lashings of the superstructure, and we smelt leather and horses three counties deep all around. We was, as you might say, in the thick of it."

" 'Ah!' says my Mr. Morshed. 'My 'orizon has indeed broadened. What a little thing is an uncle, Mr. Pyecroft, in the presence o' these glitterin' constellations! Simply ludicrous!' he says, "to waste a rocking-horse on an individual. We must socialise it. But we must get their 'eads up first. Touch off one rocket, if you please."

"I touched off a green three-pounder which rose several thousand metres, and burst into gorgeous stars. 'Reproduce the manoeuvre,' he says, 'at the other end o' this ridge – if it don't end in another cliff.' So we steamed down the ridge a mile and a half east, and then I let Jules touch off a pink rocket, or he'd ha' kissed me. That was his only way to express his emotions, so to speak. Their heads come up then all around us in the extent o' thousands. We hears bugles like cocks crowing below, and on the top of it a most impressive sound which I'd never enjoyed before because 'itherto I'd always been an inteegral part of it, so to say – the noise of

109

'ole armies gettin' under arms. They must 'ave anticipated a night attack, I imagine. Most impressive. Then we 'eard a threshin'-machine. 'Tutt! Tutt! This is childish!' says Lootenant Morshed. 'We can't wait till they've finished cutting chaff for their horses. We must make 'em understand we're not to be trifled with. Expedite 'em with another rocket, Mr. Pyecroft.'

" 'It's barely possible, sir,' I remarks, 'that that's a search-light churnin' up,' and by the time we backed into a pro-vidential chalk cutting (which was where our first tyre went pungo) she broke out to the northward, and began searching the ridge. A smart bit o' work."

" 'Twasn't a puncture. The inner tube had nipped because we skidded so," Leggatt interrupted.

"While your Mr. Leggatt was effectin' repairs, another searchlight broke out to the southward, and the two of 'em swept our ridge on both sides. Right at the west end of it they showed us the ground rising into a hill, so to speak, crowned with what looked like a little fort. Morshed saw it before the beams shut off. 'That's the key of the position!' he says. 'Occupy it at all hazards.'

" 'I haven't half got occupation for the next twenty minutes,' says your Mr. Leggatt, rootin' and blasphemin' in the dark. Mark, now, 'ow Morshed changed his tactics to suit 'is en-vironment. 'Right!' says he. 'I'll stand by the ship. Mr. Pye-croft and Jules, oblige me by doubling along the ridge to the east with all the maroons and crackers you can carry without spilling. Read the directions careful for the maroons, Mr. Pyecroft, and touch them off at half-minute intervals. Jules represents musketry an' maxim fire under your command. Remember, it's death or Salisbury Gaol! Prob'ly both!'

"By these means and some moderately 'ard runnin', we distracted 'em to the eastward. Maroons, you may not be aware, are same as bombs, with the anarchism left out. In confined spots like chalk-pits, they knock a four-point-seven silly. But you should read the directions before'and. In the intervals of the slow but well-directed fire of my cow-guns, Jules, who had found a sheep-pond in the dark a little lower down, gave what you might call a cinematograph reproduc-

110

tion o' sporadic musketry. They was large size crackers, and he concluded with the dull, sickenin' thud o' blind shells burstin' on soft ground."

"How did he manage that?" I said.

"You throw a lighted squib into water and you'll see," said Pyecroft. "Thus, then, we improvised till supplies was exhausted and the surrounding landscapes fair 'owled and 'ummed at us. The Junior Service might 'ave 'ad their doubts about the rockets, but they couldn't overlook our gunfire. Both sides tumbled out full of initiative. I told Jules no two flat-feet 'ad any right to be as happy as us, and we went back along the ridge to the derelict, and there was our Mr. Morshed apostrophin' his 'andiwork over fifty square mile o' country with 'Attend, all ye who list to hear!' out of the Fifth Reader. He'd got as far as 'And roused the shepherds o' Stonehenge, the rangers o' Beaulieu' when we come up, and he drew our attention to its truth as well as its beauty. That's rare in poetry, I'm told. He went right on to – 'The red glare on Skiddaw roused those beggers at Carlisle' – which he pointed out was poetic licence for Leith Hill. This allowed your Mr. Leggatt time to finish pumpin' up his tyres. I 'eard the sweat 'op off his nose."

"You know what it is, sir," said poor Leggatt to me.

"It warfted across my mind, as I listened to what was trarnspirin', that it might be easier to make the mess than to wipe it up, but such considerations weighed not with our valiant leader."

" 'Mr. Pyecroft,' he says, 'it can't have escaped your notice that we 'ave one angry and 'ighly intelligent army in front of us, an' another 'ighly angry and equally intelligent army in our rear. What 'ud you recommend?'

"Most men would have besought 'im to do a lateral glide while there was yet time, but all I said was: ' The rocking-horse isn't expended yet, sir.'

"He laid his hand on my shoulder. 'Pye,' says he, 'there's worse men than you in loftier places. They shall 'ave it. None the less,' he remarks, 'the ice is undeniably packing.'

"I may 'ave omitted to point out that at this juncture two large armies, both deprived of their night's sleep, was awake, as you might say, and hurryin' into each other's arms. Here endeth the second chapter."

He filled his pipe slowly. The uncle had fallen asleep. Leggat lit another cigarette.

"We then proceeded *ong automobile* along the ridge in a westerly direction towards the miniature fort which had been so kindly revealed by the searchlight, but which on inspection (your Mr. Leggatt bumped into an outlyin' reef of it) proved to be a wurzel-clump; *e'est-à-dire*, a parallelogrammatic pile of about three million mangold-wurzels, brought up there for the sheep, I suppose. On all sides, excep' the one we'd come by, the ground fell away moderately quick, and down at the bottom there was a large camp lit up an' full of harsh words of command."

" 'I said it was the key to the position,' Lootenant Morshed remarks, 'Trot out Persimmon!' which we rightly took to read, 'Un-wrap the rocking-horse.'

" 'Houp la!' says Jules in a insubordinate tone, an' slaps Persimmon on the flank.

" 'Silence!' says the Lootenant. 'This is the Royal Navy, not Newmarket'; and we carried Persimmon to the top of the mangel-wurzel clump as directed.

"Owing to the inequalities of the terrain (I *do* think your Mr. Leggatt might have had a spirit-level in his kit) he wouldn't rock free on the bed-plate, and while adjustin' him, his detachable tail fetched adrift. Our Lootenant was quick to seize the advantage.

" 'Remove that transformation,' he says. 'Substitute one Roman candle. Gas-power is superior to manual propulsion.'

"So we substituted. He arranged the *pièce de resistarnce* in the shape of large drums – not saucers, mark you – drums of coloured fire, with printed instructions, at proper distances round Persimmon. There was a brief interregnum while we dug ourselves in among the wurzels by hand. Then he touched off the fires, *not* omitting the Roman candle, and, you may take it from me, all was visible. Persimmon shone out in his naked splendour, red to port, green to starboard, and one white light at his bows, as per Board o' Trade regulations. Only he didn't so much rock, you might say, as shrug himself, in a manner of speaking, every time the candle went off. One can't have everything. But the rest surpassed our highest expectations. I think Persimmon was noblest on the starboard or green side – more like when a man thinks he's seeing mackerel in hell, don't you know? And yet I'd be the last to deprecate the effect of the port light on his teeth, or that bloodshot look in his left eye. He knew there was something going on he didn't approve of. He looked worried.'

"Did you laugh?" I said.

"I'm not much of a wag myself; nor it wasn't as if we 'ad time to allow the spectacle to sink in. The coloured fires was supposed to burn ten minutes, whereas it was obvious to the meanest capacity that the Junior Service would arrive by forced marches in about two and a half. They grarsped our topical allusion as soon as it was across the foot-lights, so to speak. They were quite chafed at it. Of course, 'ad we reflected, we might have known that exposin' illuminated rockin' horses to an army that was learnin' to ride on 'em partook of the nature of a *double entender*, as the French say – same as waggling the tiller lines at a man who's had a hang-ing in the family. I knew the cox of the *Archimandrite's* galley 'arf killed for a similar *plaisanteree*. But we never anticipated lobsters being so sensitive. That was why we shifted. We could 'ardly tear our commandin' officer away. He put his head on one side, and kept cooin'. The only thing he 'ad neglected to provide was a line of retreat; but your Mr. Leggatt – an 'eroic soul in the last stage of wet prostration – here took command of the van, or, rather, the rear-guard. We walked downhill beside him, holding on to the super-structure to prevent her capsizing. These technical details, 'owever, are beyond me." He waved his pipe towards Leggatt.

"I saw there was two deepish ruts leadin' down'ill some-where," said Leggatt. "That was when the soldiers stopped laughin', and begun to run uphill."

"Stroll, lovey, stroll!" Pyecroft corrected. 'The Dervish rush took place later."

"So I laid her in these ruts. That was where she must 'ave scraped her silencer a bit. Then they turned sharp right – the ruts did – and then she stopped bonnet-high in a manure-heap, sir; but I'll swear it was all of a one in three gradient. I think it was a barnyard. We waited there," said Leggatt.

"But not for long," said Pyecroft. "The lights were towering out of the drums on the position we 'ad so valiantly abandoned; and the Junior Service was escaladin' in *en masse*. When numerous bodies of 'ighly trained men arrive simultaneous in the same latitude from opposite directions, each remarking briskly, 'What the 'ell did you do *that* for?' detonation, as you might say, is practically assured. They didn't ask for extraneous aids. If we'd come out with sworn affidavits of what we'd done they wouldn't 'ave believed us. They wanted each other's company exclusive. Such was the effect of Persimmon on their clarss feelings. Idol'try *I* call it! Events transpired with the utmost velocity and rapidly increasing pressures. There was a few remarks about Dicky Bridoon and mechanical horses, and then some one was smacked – hard by the sound – in the middle of a remark."

"That was the man who kept calling for the Forty-fifth Dragoons," said Leggatt. "He got as far as Drag..."

"Was it?" said Pyecroft dreamily. "Well, he couldn't say they didn't come. They all came, and they all fell to arguin' whether the Infantry should 'ave Persimmon for a regimental pet or the Cavalry should keep him for stud purposes. Hence the issue was soon clouded with mangold-wurzels. Our commander said we 'ad sowed the good seed, and it was bearing abundant fruit. (They weigh between four and seven pounds apiece.) Seein' the children 'ad got over their shyness, and 'ad really begun to play games, we backed out o' the pit and went down, by steps, to the camp below, no man, as you might say, making us afraid. Here we enjoyed a front view of the battle, which rolled with renewed impetus, owing to both sides receiving strong reinforcements every minute. All arms were freely represented; Cavalry, on this occasion only, acting in concert with Artillery. They argued the relative merits of horses *versus* feet, so to say, but they didn't neglect Persimmon. The wounded rolling downhill with the wurzels informed us that he had long ago been socialised, and the smallest souvenirs were worth a man's life. Speaking broadly, the Junior Service appeared to be a shade out of 'and, if I may venture so far. They did *not* pay prompt and unhesitating obedience to the 'Retires' or the 'Cease Fires' or the 'For 'Eaven's sake come to bed, ducky' of their officers, who, I regret to say, were 'otly embroiled at the heads of their respective units."

"How did you find that out?" I asked.

"On account of Lootenant Morshed going to the Mess tent to call on his uncle and raise a drink; but all hands had gone to the front. We thought we 'eard somebody bathing behind the tent, and we found an oldish gentleman tryin' to drown a boy in knickerbockers in a horse-trough. He kept him under with a bicycle, so to speak. He 'ad nearly accomplished his fell design, when we frustrated him. He was in a highly malleable condition and full o' *juice de spree*. 'Arsk not what I am,' he says. 'My wife 'll tell me that quite soon enough. Arsk rather what I've been," he says. 'I've been dinin' here,' he says, 'I commanded 'em in the Eighties,' he says, 'and, Gawd forgive me,' he says, sobbin' 'eavily, 'I've spent this holy evening telling their Colonel they was a set of educated inefficients. Hark to 'em!' We could, without strainin' ourselves; but how *he* picked up the gentle murmur of his own corps in that on-the-knee party up the hill I don't know. 'They've marched and fought thirty mile to-day,' he shouts, 'and now they're tearin' the intes*tines* out of the Cavalry up yonder! They won't stop this side the gates o' Delhi," he says. "I commanded their ancestors. There's nothing wrong with the Service," he says, wringing out his trousers on his lap. ''Eaven pardon me for doubtin' 'em! Same old game – same young beggars.'

"The boy in the knickerbockers, languishing on a chair, puts in a claim for one drink. 'Let him go dry,' says our friend in shirt-tails. 'He's a reporter. He run into me on his filthy bicycle and he asked me if I could furnish 'im with particulars about the mutiny in the Army. You false-'earted proletarian publicist,' he says, shakin' his finger at 'im – for he was reelly annoyed – 'I'll teach you to defile what you can't comprehend! When my regiment's in a state o' mutiny, I'll do myself the honour of informing you personally. You particularly

115

ignorant and very narsty little man,' he says, 'you're no better than a dhobi's donkey! If there wasn't dirty linen to wash, you'd starve,' he says, 'and why I haven't drowned you will be the lastin' regret of my life.'

"Well, we sat with 'em and 'ad drinks for about half-an-hour in front of the Mess tent. He'd ha' killed the reporter if there hadn't been witnesses, and the reporter might have taken notes of the battle; so we acted as two-way buffers, in a sense. I don't hold with the Press mingling up with Service matters. They draw false conclusions. Now, mark you, at a moderate estimate, there were seven thousand men in the fighting line, half of 'em hurt in their professional feelings, an' the other half rubbin' in the liniment, as you might say. All due to Persimmon! If you 'adn't seen it you wouldn't 'ave believed it. And yet, mark you, not a single unit of 'em even resorted to his belt. They confined themselves to natural producks – hands and the wurzels. I thought Jules was havin' fits, till it trarnspired the same thought had impressed him in the French language. He called in *incroyable*, I believe. Seven thousand men, with seven thousand rifles, belts, and bayonets, in a violently agitated condition, and not a ungenteel blow struck from first to last. The old gentleman drew our attention to it as well. It was quite noticeable.

"Lack of ammunition was the primerry cause of the battle ceasin'. A Brigade-Major came in, wipin' his nose on both cuffs, and sayin' he 'ad 'ad snuff. The brigadier-uncle followed. He was, so to speak, sneezin'. We thought it best to shift our moorings without attractin' attention; so we shifted. They 'ad called the cows 'ome by then. The Junior Service was going to bye-bye all round us, as happy as the ship's monkey when he's been playin' with the paints, and Lootenant Morshed and Jules kept bowin' to port and starboard of the super-structure, acknowledgin' the unstinted applause which the multitude would 'ave given 'em if they'd known the facts. On the other 'and, as your Mr. Leggatt observed, they might 'ave killed us.

"That would have been about five bells in the middle watch, say half-past two. A well-spent evening. There was but little to be gained by entering Portsmouth at that hour, so we turned off on the grass (this was after we had found a road under us), and we cast anchors out at the stern and prayed for the day.

"But your Mr. Leggatt he had to make and mend tyres all our watch below. It trarnspired she had been running on the rim o' two or three wheels, which, very properly, he hadn't reported till the close of the action. And that's the reason for your four new tyres. Mr. Morshed was of opinion you'd earned 'em. Do you dissent?"

I stretched out my hand, which Pyecroft crushed to pulp. "No, Pye," I said, deeply moved, "I agree entirely. But what happened to Jules?"

"We returned him to his own Navy after breakfast. He wouldn't have kept much longer without some one in his own language to tell it to. I don't know any man I ever took more compassion on than Jules. 'Is sufferings swelled him up centimetres, and all he could do on the Hard was to kiss Lootenant Morshed and me, *and* your Mr. Leggatt. He deserved that much. A cordial beggar."

Pyecroft looked at the washed cups on the table, and the low sunshine on my car's back in the yard.

"'Too early to drink to him," he said. "But I feel it just the same."

The uncle, sunk in his chair, snored a little; the canary answered with a shrill lullaby. Pyecroft picked up the duster, threw it over the cage, put his finger to his lips, and we tiptoed out into the shop, while Leggatt brought the car round.

"I'll look out for the news in the papers," I said, as I got in.

"Oh, we short-circuited that! Nothing trarnspired excep' a statement to the effect that some Territorial battalions had played about with turnips at the conclusion of the manœuvres. The taxpayer don't know all he gets for his money. Farewell!"

We moved off just in time to be blocked by a regiment coming towards the station to entrain for London.

"Beg your pardon, sir," said a sergeant in charge of the

baggage, "but would you mind backin' a bit till we get the waggons past?"

"Certainly," I said. "You don't happen to have a rocking-horse among your kit, do you?"

The rattle of our reverse drowned his answer, but I saw his eyes. One of them was blackish-green, about four days old.

THE CENTAURS

This poem first appeared in "Debits and Credits" the second last of Kipling's collections of stories. At the time these were written he was wracked by ill health and his vision was sombre. He was looking back to the central theme which pervaded much of his writing of "The Bonds of Discipline", illustrating it by the mythological centaurs, half men, half horses, being trained to endure those very bonds and to triumph over them under the eyes of their mentor, Chiron.

THE CENTAURS

Up came the young Centaur-colts from the plains they
    were fathered in –
Curious awkward, afraid.
Burrs on their hocks and their tails, they were branded and
    gathered in
Mobs and run up to the yard to be made.

Starting and shying at straws, with sidelings and
    plungings,
  Buckings and whirlings and bolts;
Greener than grass, but full-ripe for their bridlings and
    lungings,
  Up to the yards and to Chiron they bustled the colts . . .

118

First the light web and the cavesson; then the linked keys
　　To jingle and turn on the tongue. Then, with cocked
　　　　ears,
The hours of watching and envy, while comrades at ease
　　Passaged and backed, making naught of these terrible
　　　　gears.

Next, over-pride and its price at the low-seeming fence,
　　Too oft and too easily taken – the world-beheld fall!
And none in the yard except Chiron to doubt the
　　　　immense,
　　Irretrievable shame of it all! ...

Last, the trained squadron, full-charge – the sound of a
　　　　going
　　Through dust and spun clods, and strong kicks, pelted
　　　　in as they went,
And repaid at top-speed; till the order to halt without
　　　　slowing
　　Brought every colt on his haunches – and Chiron
　　　　content!

8

THE FOX MEDITATES

This was another late poem, and for once, in his later years, Kipling changed his sombre mood and returned to the time and theme of his long ago light-hearted verses. Aficionados will note that the metre here is the same as "The Vicar of Bray" upon whom the anonymous scribe conferred immortality in Regency times. Kipling, when he wished could write parodies with the best. In these verses he combined his knowledge of history and how he could adapt it to his purposes, with his feeling for the chase, and the changes which had taken place down the years. As is shown, he never lost his fascination with the fox and his ways across the centuries, nor his admiration for Surtees, the finest of his chroniclers through the sayings of John Jorrocks M.F.H. So it is fitting that one of the very last poems he wrote should celebrate the wiliest quarry against which horsemen have pitted their wits and risked their necks since the days of Nimrod.

THE FOX MEDITATES

When Samson set my brush a'fire,
    To spoil the Timnites' barley,
I made my point for Leicestershire,
    And left Philistia early.
Through Gath and Rankesborough Gorse, I fled,
    And took the Coplow Road, sir!
And was a Gentleman in Red
    When all the Quorn wore woad, sir!

When Rome lay massed on Hadrian's Wall,
  And nothing much was doing,
Her bored Centurions heard my call
  O' nights when I went wooing.
They raised a pack – they ran it well
  (For I was there to run 'em)
From Aesica to Carter Fell,
  And down North Tyne to Hunnum.

When William landed, hot for blood,
  And Harold's hosts were smitten,
I lay at earth in Battle Wood
  While Domesday Book was written.
Whatever harm he did to man,
  I owe him pure affection,
For in his righteous reign began
  The first of Game protection.

When Charles, my namesake, lost his mask,
  And Oliver dropped his'n,
I set those Northern Squires a task,
  To keep 'em out of prison.
In boots as big as milking-pails,
  With holsters on the pommel,
They chevied me across the Dales
  Instead of fighting Cromwell.

When thrifty Walpole took the helm,
  And hedging came in fashion,
The March of Progress gave my realm
  Enclosure and Plantation.
'Twas then, to soothe their discontent,
  I showed each pounded Master,
However fast the Commons went,
  I went a little faster!

When Pigg and Jorrocks held the stage,
  And Steam had linked the Shires,
I broke the staid Victorian age
  To posts, and rails and wires.

Then fifty mile was none too far
    To go by train to cover,
Till some dam' sutler pupped a Car,
    And decent sport was over!

When men grew shy of hunting stag,
    For fear the Law might try 'em,
The Car put up an average bag
    Of twenty dead per diem.
Then every road was made a rink
    For Coroners to sit on;
And so began, in skid and stink,
    The real blood-sports of Britain!

9

★ MY SON'S WIFE
★ IN PARTIBUS

Here Kipling is letting himself go with a vengeance at the intellectuals and "the immoderate left", their pretensions and insincerities, and the redemption of his protagonist, Midmore, by country pursuits and country people. It is extraordinary how well this story, written over half a century ago, stands up today and with a few minor adjustments such as pounds, shillings and pence, it could have been written yesterday. Largely ignored by critics perhaps because usually they, themselves, are drawn from "the immoderate left", it remains one of Kipling's most effective stories, told with a sure hand and without a false note.

There is some excellent horse-coping and hunting in Kipling's account of Midmore's regeneration with its moral of the clash and contradictions between the town-dwellers who take their prejudices to the country which they do not and will not understand and the country people to whom they are as strange as aliens from another planet. It is only the few, like Midmore, who once bewitched and converted can slough off their former – and false – skin.

It enables Kipling, too, to bring in one of his favourite authors, Surtees, who plays his part in the conversion of Midmore. Kipling never hunted himself but he admired those who did; did he not write:

> Reach me my *Handley Cross* again,
> My run, where never danger lurks, is
> With Jorrocks and his deathless train –
> Pigg, Binjimin, and Artexerxes.

My Son's Wife also contains an off-hand, low-key, love story, and so completes what we said at the outset: here he has written of "women and horses, and love and war," and it complements the sentiments expressed in *In Partibus*, penned twenty years earlier when he was alone and lonely in London. It is included here as a *finale* to show Kipling's distaste, which lasted all his life, for things too much of the mind and his longing to be amongst uncomplicated people whose passions and purposes he turned into song and story and distilled into literature as never done before – or since.

"MY SON'S WIFE"

He had suffered from the disease of the century since his early youth, and before he was thirty he was heavily marked with it. He and a few friends had rearranged Heaven very comfortably, but the reorganisation of Earth, which they called Society, was even greater fun. It demanded Work in the shape of many taxi-rides daily; hours of brilliant talk with brilliant talkers; some sparkling correspondence; a few silences (but on the understanding that their own turn should come soon) while other people expounded philo-sophies; and a fair number of picture-galleries, tea-fights, concerts, theatres, music-halls, and cinema shows; the whole trimmed with love-making to women whose hair smelt of cigarette-smoke. Such strong days sent Frankwell Midmore back to his flat assured that he and his friends had helped the World a step nearer the Truth, the Dawn, and the New Order.

His temperament, he said, led him more towards concrete data than abstract ideas. People who investigate detail are apt to be tired at the day's end. The same temperament, or it may have been a woman, made him early attach himself to the Immoderate Left of his Cause in the capacity of an experimenter in Social Relations. And since the Immoderate Left contains plenty of women anxious to help earnest inquirers with large independent incomes to arrive at evaluations of essentials, Frankwell Midmore's lot was far from contemptible.

At that hour Fate chose to play with him. A widowed aunt, widely separated by nature, and more widely by marriage, from all that Midmore's mother had ever been or desired to be, died and left him possessions. Mrs. Midmore, having that summer embraced a creed which denied the existence of death, naturally could not stoop to burial; but Midmore had to leave London for the dank country at a season when Social Regeneration works best through long, cushioned conferences, two by two, after tea. There he faced the bracing ritual of the British funeral, and was wept at across the raw grave by an elderly coffin-shaped female with a long nose, who called him "Master Frankie"; and there he was congratulated behind an echoing top-hat by a man he mistook for a mute, who turned out to be his aunt's lawyer. He wrote his mother next day, after a bright account of the funeral:

"So far as I can understand, she has left me between four and five hundred a year. It all comes from Ther Land, as they call it down here. The unspeakable attorney, Sperrit, and a green-eyed daughter, who hums to herself as she tramps but is silent on all subjects except 'huntin',' insisted on taking me to see it. Ther Land is brown and green in alternate slabs like chocolate and pistachio cakes, speckled with occasional peasants who do not utter. In case it should not be wet enough there is a wet brook in the middle of it. Ther House is by the brook. I shall look into it later. If there should be any little memento of Jenny that you care for, let me know. Didn't you tell me that mid-Victorian furniture is coming into the market again? Jenny's old maid – it is called Rhoda Dolbie – tells me that Jenny promised it thirty pounds a year. The will does not. Hence, I suppose, the tears at the funeral. But that is close on ten per cent of the income. I fancy Jenny

125

has destroyed all her private papers and records of her *vie intime* if, indeed, life be possible in such a place. The Sperrit man told me that if I had means of my own I might come and live on Ther Land. I didn't tell him how much I would pay not to! I cannot think it right that any human being should exercise mastery over others in the merciless fashion our tom-fool social system permits; so, as it is all mine, I intend to sell it whenever the unholy Sperrit can find a purchaser."

And he went to Mr. Sperrit with the idea next day, just before returning to town.

"Quite so," said the lawyer. "I see your point, of course. But the house itself is rather old-fashioned – hardly the type purchasers demand nowadays. There's no park, of course, and the bulk of the land is let to a life-tenant, a Mr. Sidney. As long as he pays his rent, he can't be turned out, and even if he didn't – Mr. Sperrit's face relaxed a shade – "you might have a difficulty."

"The property brings four hundred a year, I understand," said Midmore.

"Well, hardly – ha-ardly. Deducting land and income tax, tithes, fire insurance, cost of collection and repairs of course, it returned two hundred and eighty-four pounds last year. The repairs are rather a large item – owing to the brook. I call it Liris – out of Horace, you know."

Midmore looked at his watch impatiently.

"I suppose you can find somebody to buy it?" he repeated.

"We will do our best, of course, if those are your instructions. Then, that is all except" – here Midmore half rose, but Mr. Sperrit's little grey eyes held his large brown ones firmly "except about Rhoda Dolbie, Mrs. Werf's maid. I may tell you that we did not draw up your aunt's last will. She grew secretive towards the last – elderly people often do – and had it done in London. I expect her memory failed her, or she mislaid her notes. She used to put them in her spectacle case. ... My motor only takes eight minutes to get to the station, Mr. Midmore ... but, as I was saying, whenever she made her will with *us*, Mrs. Werf always left Rhoda thirty pounds per annum. Charlie, the wills!" A clerk with a baldish head and a long nose dealt documents on to the table like

126

cards, and breathed heavily behind Midmore. "It's in no sense a legal obligation, of course," said Mr. Sperrit. "Ah, that one is dated January the 11th, eighteen eighty-nine."

Midmore looked at his watch again and found himself saying with no good grace: "Well, I suppose she'd better have it – for the present at any rate."

He escaped with an uneasy feeling that two hundred and fifty-four pounds a year was not exactly four hundred, and that Charlie's long nose annoyed him. Then he returned, first-class, to his own affairs.

Of the two, perhaps three, experiments in Social Relations which he had then in hand, one interested him acutely. It had run for some months and promised most variegated and interesting developments, on which he dwelt luxuriously all the way to town. When he reached his flat he was not well prepared for a twelve-page letter explaining, in the diction of the Immoderate Left which rubricates its I's and illuminates its T's, that the lady had realised greater attractions in another Soul. She re-stated, rather than pleaded, the gospel of the Immoderate Left as her justification, and ended in an impassioned demand for her right to express herself in and on her own life, through which, she pointed out, she could pass but once. She added that if, later, she should discover Midmore was "essentially complementary to her needs," she would tell him so. That Midmore had himself written much the same sort of epistle – barring the hint of return – to a woman of whom his needs for self-expression had caused him to weary three years before, did not assist him in the least. He expressed himself to the gas-fire in terms essential but not complimentary. Then he reflected on the detached criticism of his best friends and her best friends, male and female, with whom he and she and others had talked so openly while their gay adventure was in flower. He recalled, too – this must have been about midnight – her analysis from every angle, remote and most intimate, of the mate to whom she had been adjudged under the base convention which is styled marriage. Later, at that bad hour when the cattle wake for a little, he remembered her in other aspects and went down into the hell appointed; desolate, desiring, with no

127

God to call upon. About eleven o'clock next morning Eliphaz the Temanite, Bildad the Shuhite, and Zophar the Naamathite called upon him "for they had made appointment together" to see how he took it; but the janitor told them that Job had gone – into the country, he believed.

Midmore's relief when he found his story was not written across his aching temples for Mr. Sperrit to read – the defeated lover, like the successful one, believes all earth privy to his soul – was put down by Mr. Sperrit to quite different causes. He led him into a morning-room. The rest of the house seemed to be full of people, singing to a loud piano idiotic songs about cows, and the hall smelt of damp cloaks.

"It's our evening to take the winter cantata," Mr. Sperrit explained. "It's 'High Tide on the Coast of Lincolnshire.' I hoped you'd come back. There are scores of little things to settle. As for the house, of course, it stands ready for you at any time. I couldn't get Rhoda out of it – or could Charlie for that matter. She's the sister, isn't she, of the nurse who brought you down here when you were four, she says, to recover from measles?"

"Is she? Was I?" said Midmore through the bad tastes in his mouth. "D'you suppose I could stay there the night?"

Thirty joyous young voices shouted appeal to some one to leave their "pipes of parsley 'ollow – 'ollow – 'ollow!" Mr. Sperrit had to raise his voice above the din.

"Well, if I asked you to stay *here*, I should never hear the last of it from Rhoda. She's a little cracked, of course, but the soul of devotion and capable of anything. *Ne sit ancillae*, you know."

"Thank you. Then I'll go. I'll walk." He tumbled out dazed and sick into the winter twilight, and sought the square house by the brook.

It was not a dignified entry, because when the door was unchained and Rhoda exclaimed, he took two valiant steps into the hall and then fainted – as men sometimes will after twenty-two hours of strong emotion and little food.

"I'm sorry," he said when he could speak. He was lying at the foot of the stairs, his head on Rhoda's lap.

128

"Your 'ome is your castle, sir," was the reply in his hair. "I smelt it wasn't drink. You lay on the sofa till I get your supper."

She settled him in a drawing-room hung with yellow silk, heavy with the smell of dead leaves and oil lamp. Something murmured soothingly in the background and overcame the noises in his head. He thought he heard horses' feet on wet gravel and a voice singing about ships and flocks and grass. It passed close to the shuttered bay-window.

> But each will mourn his own, she saith,
> And sweeter woman ne'er drew breath
> Than my son's wife, Elizabeth . . .
> Cusha – cusha – cusha – calling.

The hoofs broke into a canter as Rhoda entered with the tray. "And then I'll put you to bed," she said. "Sidney's coming in the morning." Midmore asked no questions. He dragged his poor bruised soul to bed and would have pitied it all over again, but the food and warm sherry and water drugged him to instant sleep.

Rhoda's voice wakened him, asking whether he would have "'ip, foot, or sitz," which he understood were the baths of the establishment. "Suppose you try all three," she suggested. "They're all yours, you know, sir."

He would have renewed his sorrows with the daylight, but her words struck him pleasantly. Everything his eyes opened upon was his very own to keep for ever. The carved four-post Chippendale bed, obviously worth hundreds; the wavy walnut William and Mary chairs – he had seen worse ones labelled twenty guineas apiece; and oval medallion mirror; the delicate eighteenth-century wire fireguard; the heavy brocaded curtains were his – all his. So, too, a great garden full of birds that faced him when he shaved; a mulberry tree, a sun-dial, and a dull, steel-coloured brook that murmured level with the edge of a lawn a hundred yards away. Peculiarly and privately his own was the smell of sausages and coffee that he sniffed at the head of the wide square landing, all set round with mysterious doors and Bartolozzi prints. He spent

129

two hours after breakfast in exploring his new possessions. His heart leaped up at such things as sewing-machines, a rubber-tyred bath-chair in a tiled passage, a malachite-headed Malacca cane, boxes and boxes of unopened stationery, seal-rings, bunches of keys, and at the bottom of a steel-net reticule a little leather purse with seven pounds ten shillings in gold and eleven shillings in silver.

"You used to play with that when my sister brought you down here after your measles," said Rhoda as he slipped the money into his pocket. "Now, this was your pore dear auntie's business-room." She opened a low door. "Oh, I forgot about Mr. Sidney! There he is." An enormous old man with rheumy red eyes that blinked under downy white eye-brows sat in an Empire chair, his cap in his hands. Rhoda withdrew sniffing. The man looked Midmore over in silence, then jerked a thumb towards the door. "I reckon she told you who I be," he began. "I'm the only farmer you've got. Nothin' goes off my place 'thout it walks on its own feet. What about my pig-pound?"

"Well, what about it?" said Midmore.

"That's just what I be come about. The County Councils are getting more particular. Did ye know there was swine fever at Pashell's? There *be*. It'll 'ave to be in brick."

"Yes," said Midmore politely.

"I've bin at your aunt that was, plenty times about it. I don't say she wasn't a just woman, but she didn't read the lease same way I did. I be used to bein' put upon, but there's no doing any longer 'thout that pig-pound."

"When would you like it?" Midmore asked. It seemed the easiest road to take.

"Any time or other suits me, I reckon. He ain't thrivin' where he is, an' I paid eighteen shillin' for him." He crossed his hands on his stick and gave no further sign of life.

"Is that all?" Midmore stammered.

"All now – excep'" – he glanced fretfully at the table beside him – "excep' my usuals. Where's that Rhoda?"

Midmore rang the bell. Rhoda came in with a bottle and a glass. The old man helped himself to four stiff fingers, rose in one piece, and stumped out. At the door he cried ferociously:

130

"Don't suppose it's any odds to you whether I'm drowned
or not, but them floodgates want a wheel and winch, they
do. I be too old for liftin' 'em with the bar – my time o'
life."

"Good riddance if 'e was drowned," said Rhoda. "But
don't you mind him. He's only amusin' himself. Your pore
dear auntie used to give 'im 'is usual – 'tisn't the whisky *you*
drink – an' send 'im about 'is business."

"I see. Now, is a pig-pound the same thing as a pig-sty?"

Rhoda nodded. "'E needs one, too, but 'e ain't entitled to
it. You look at 'is lease – third drawer on the left in that
Bombay cab'net – an' next time 'e comes you ask 'im to read
it. That'll choke 'im off, because 'e can't!"

There was nothing in Midmore's past to teach him the
message and significance of a hand-written lease of the late
'eighties, but Rhoda interpreted.

"It don't mean anything reelly," was her cheerful conclusion, "excep' you mustn't get rid of him anyhow, an' 'e
can do what 'e likes always. Lucky for us 'e *do* farm; and if it
wasn't for 'is woman – "

"Oh, there's a Mrs. Sidney, is there?"

"Lor, *no!*" The Sidneys don't marry. They keep. That's his
fourth since – to my knowledge. He was a takin' man from
the first."

"Any families?"

"They'd be grown up by now if there was, wouldn't they?
But you can't spend all your days considerin' 'is interests.
That's what gave your pore aunt 'er indigestion. 'Ave you
seen the gun-room?"

Midmore held strong views on the immorality of taking life
for pleasure. But there was no denying that the late Colonel
Werf's seventy-guinea breechloaders were good at their
filthy job. He loaded one, took it out and pointed – merely
pointed – it at a cock-pheasant which rose out of a shrubbery
behind the kitchen, and the flaming bird came down in a
long slant on the lawn, stone dead. Rhoda from the scullery
said it was a lovely shot, and told him lunch was ready.

He spent the afternoon gun in one hand, a map in the
other, beating the bounds of his lands. They lay altogether in

131

a shallow, uninteresting valley, flanked with woods and bisected by a brook. Up stream was his own house; down stream, less than half a mile, a low red farm-house squatted in an old orchard, beside what looked like small lock-gates on the Thames. There was no doubt as to ownership. Mr. Sidney saw him while yet far off, and bellowed at him about pig-pounds and flood-gates. These last were two great sliding shutters of weedy oak across the brook, which were prised up inch by inch with a crowbar along a notched strip of iron, and when Sidney opened them they at once let out half the water. Midmore watched it shrink between its aldered banks like some conjuring trick. This, too, was his very own.

"I see," he said. "How interesting! Now, what's that bell for?" he went on, pointing to an old ship's bell in a rude belfry at the end of an outhouse. "Was that a chapel once?" The red-eyed giant seemed to have difficulty in expressing himself for a moment and blinked savagely.

"Yes," he said at last. "My chapel. When you 'ear that bell ring you'll 'ear something. Nobody but me ud put up with it – but I reckon it don't make any odds to you." He slammed the gates down again, and the brook rose behind them with a suck and a grunt.

Midmore moved off, conscious that he might be safer with Rhoda to hold his conversational hand. As he passed the front of the farm-house a smooth fat woman, with neatly parted grey hair under a widow's cap, curtsied to him deferentially through the window. By every teaching of the Immoderate Left she had a perfect right to express herself in any way she pleased, but the curtsey revolted him. And on his way home he was hailed from behind a hedge by a manifest idiot with no roof to his mouth, who hallooed and danced round him.

"What did that beast want?" he demanded Rhoda at tea.

"Jimmy? He only wanted to know if you 'ad any telegrams to send. 'E'll go anywhere so long as 'tisn't across running water. That gives 'im 'is seizures. Even talkin' about it for fun like makes 'im shake.

"But why isn't he where he can be properly looked after?"

"What 'arm's 'e doing? 'E's a love-child, but 'is family can pay for 'im. If 'e was locked up 'e'd die all off at once, like a wild rabbit. Won't you, please, look at the drive, sir?"

Midmore looked in the fading light. The neat gravel was pitted with large roundish holes, and there was a punch or two of the same sort on the lawn.

"That's your 'unt comin' 'ome," Rhoda explained. "Your pore dear auntie always let 'em use our drive for a short cut after the Colonel died. The Colonel wouldn't so much because he preserved; but your auntie was always an 'orsewoman till 'er sciatica."

"Isn't there some one who can rake it over or – something?" said Midmore vaguely.

"Oh, yes. You'll never see it in the morning, but – you was out when they came 'ome an' Mister Fisher – he's the Master – told me to tell you with 'is compliments that if you wasn't preservin' and cared to 'old to the old understandin', 'is gravel-pit is at your service same as before. 'E thought, perhaps, you mightn't know, and it 'ad slipped my mind to tell you. It's good gravel, Mister Fisher's, and it binds beautiful on the drive. We 'ave to draw it, o' course, from the pit, but – "

Midmore looked at her helplessly.

"Rhoda," said he, "what am I supposed to do?"

"Oh, let 'em come through," she replied. "You never know. You may want to 'unt yourself some day."

That evening it rained and his misery returned on him, the worse for having been diverted. At last he was driven to paw over a few score books in a panelled room called the library, and realised with horror what the late Colonel Werf's mind must have been in his prime. The volumes smelt of a dead world as strongly as they did of mildew. He opened and thrust them back, one after another, till crude coloured illustrations of men on horses held his eye. He began at random and read a little, moved into the drawing-room with the volume, and settled down by the fire still reading. It was a foul world into which he peeped for the first time – a heavy-eating, hard-drinking hell of horse-copers, swindlers, match-making mothers, economically dependent virgins selling

133

themselves blushingly for cash and lands: Jews, tradesmen, and all ill-considered spawn of Dickens-and-horsedung characters (I give Midmore's own criticism), but he read on, fascinated, and behold, from the pages leaped, as it were, the brother of the red-eyed man of the brook, bellowing at a landlord (here Midmore realised that *he* was that very animal) for new barns; and another man who, like himself again, objected to hoof-marks on gravel. Outrageous as thought and conception were, the stuff seemed to have the rudiments of observation. He dug out other volumes by the same author, till Rhoda came in with a silver candlestick.

"Rhoda," said he, "did you ever hear about a character called James Pigg – and Batsey?"

"Why, o' course," said she. "The Colonel used to come into the kitchen in 'is dressin'-gown an' read us all those Jorrockses."

"Oh, Lord!" said Midmore, and went to bed with a book called *Handley Cross* under his arm, and a lonelier Columbus into a stranger world the wet-ringed moon never looked upon.

* * *

Here we omit much. But Midmore never denied that for the epicure in sensation the urgent needs of an ancient house, as interpreted by Rhoda pointing to daylight through attic-tiles held in place by moss, gives an edge to the pleasure of Social Research elsewhere. Equally he found that the reaction following prolonged research loses much of its grey terror if one knows one can at will bathe the soul in the society of plumbers (all the water-pipes had chronic appendicitis), village idiots (Jimmy had taken Midmore under his weak wing and camped daily at the drive-gates), and a giant with red eyelids whose every action is an unpredictable outrage.

Towards spring Midmore filled his house with a few friends of the Immoderate Left. It happened to be the day when, all things and Rhoda working together, a cartload of bricks, another of sand, and some bags of lime had been despatched to build Sidney his almost daily-demanded pig-pound. Midmore took his friends across the flat fields with some idea of showing them Sidney as a type of "the peasantry." They hit the minute when Sidney, hoarse with rage, was ordering bricklayer, mate, carts and all off his premises. The visitors disposed themselves to listen.

"You never give me no notice about changin' the pig," Sidney shouted. The pig – at least eighteen inches long – reared on end in the old sty and smiled at the company.

"But, my good man – " Midmore opened.

"I ain't! For aught you know I be a dam' sight worse than you be. You can't come and be'ave arbit'ry with me. You –are be'avin' arbit'ry! All you men go clean away an' don't set foot on my land till I bid ye."

"But you asked" – Midmore felt his voice jump up – "to have the pig-pound built."

"'Spose I did. That's no reason you shouldn't send me notice to change the pig. 'Comin' down on me like this 'thout warnin'! That pig's got to be got into the cowshed an' all."

"Then open the door and let him run in," said Midmore.

"Don't you be'ave arbit'ry with *me*! Take all your dam' men 'ome off my land. I won't be treated arbit'ry."

The carts moved off without a word, and Sidney went into the house and slammed the door.

"Now, I hold that is enormously significant," said a visitor. "Here you have the logical outcome of centuries of feudal oppression – the frenzy of fear." The company looked at Midmore with grave pain.

"But he *did* worry my life out about his pig-sty," was all Midmore found to say.

Others took up the parable and proved to him if he only held true to the gospels of the Immoderate Left the earth would soon be covered with "jolly little" pig-sties, built in the intervals of morris-dancing by "the peasant" himself.

Midmore felt grateful when the door opened again and Mr. Sidney invited them all to retire to the road which, he pointed out, was public. As they turned the corner of the house, a smooth-faced woman in a widow's cap curtsied to each of them through the window.

Instantly they drew pictures of that woman's lot, deprived of all vehicle for self-expression – "the set grey life and apathetic end," one quoted – and they discussed the tremendous significance of village theatricals. Even a month ago Midmore would have told them all that he knew and Rhoda had dropped about Sidney's forms of self-expression. Now, for some strange reason, he was content to let the talk run on from village to metropolitan and world drama.

Rhoda advised him after the visitors left that "if he wanted to do that again" he had better go up to town.

"But we only sat on cushions on the floor," said her master.

"They're too old for romps," she retorted, "an' it's only the beginning of things. I've seen what *I've* seen. Besides, they talked and laughed in the passage going to their baths – such as took 'em."

"Don't be a fool, Rhoda," said Midmore. No man – unless he has loved her – will casually dismiss a woman on whose lap he has laid his head.

"Very good," she snorted, "but that cuts both ways. An' now, you go down to Sidney's this evenin' and put him where he ought to be. He was in his right about you givin' 'im notice about changin' the pig, but he 'adn't any right to turn it up before your company. No manners, no pig-pound. He'll understand."

Midmore did his best to make him. He found himself reviling the old man in speech and with a joy quite new in all his experience. He wound up – it was a plagiarism from a plumber – by telling Mr. Sidney that he looked like a turkey-cock, had the morals of a parish bull, and need never hope for a new pig-pound as long as he or Midmore lived.

"Very good," said the giant. "I reckon you thought you 'ad something against me, and now you've come down an' told it me like man to man. Quite right. I don't bear malice. Now, you send along those bricks an' sand, an' I'll make a do to build the pig-pound myself. If you look at my lease you'll find out you're bound to provide me materials for the repairs. Only – only I thought there'd be no 'arm in my askin' you to do it throughout like."

136

Midmore fairly gasped. "Then, why the devil did you turn my carts back when – when I sent them up here to do it throughout for you?"

Mr. Sidney sat down on the floodgates, his eyebrows knitted in thought.

"I'll tell you," he said slowy. "'T'was too dam' like cheatin' a suckin' baby. My woman, she said so too."

For a few seconds the teachings of the Immoderate Left, whose humour is all their own, wrestled with those of Mother Earth, who has her own humours. Then Midmore laughed till he could scarcely stand. In due time Mr. Sidney laughed too – crowing and wheezing crescendo till it broke from him in roars. They shook hands, and Midmore went home grateful that he had held his tongue among his companions.

When he reached his house he met three or four men and women on horseback, very muddy indeed, coming down the drive. Feeling hungry himself, he asked them if they were hungry. They said they were, and he bade them enter. Jimmy took their horses, who seemed to know him. Rhoda took their battered hats, led the women upstairs for hairpins, and presently fed them all with tea-cakes, poached eggs, anchovy toast, and drinks from a coromandel-wood liqueur case which Midmore had never known that he possessed.

"And I *will* say," said Miss Connie Sperrit, her spurred foot on the fender and a smoking muffin in her whip hand, "Rhoda does one top-hole. She always did since I was eight."

"Seven, Miss, was when you began to 'unt," said Rhoda, setting down more buttered toast.

"And so," the M.F.H. was saying to Midmore, "when he got to your brute Sidney's land, we had to whip 'em off. It's a regular Alsatia for 'em. They know it. Why" – he dropped his voice – "I don't want to say anything against Sidney as your tenant, of course, but I do believe the old scoundrel's perfectly capable of putting down poison."

"Sidney's capable of anything," said Midmore with immense feeling; but once again he held his tongue. They were

137

a queer community; yet when they had stamped and jingled out to their horses again, the house felt hugely big and disconcerting.

This may be reckoned the conscious beginning of his double life. It ran in odd channels that summer – a riding school, for instance, near Hayes Common and a shooting ground near Wormwood Scrubs. A man who had been saddle-galled or shoulder-bruised for half the day is not at his London best of evenings; and when the bills for his amusements came in he curtails his expenses in other directions. So a cloud settled on Midmore's name. His London world talked of a hardening of heart and a tightening of purse-strings which signified disloyalty to the Cause. One man, a confidant of the old expressive days, attacked him robustiously and demanded account of his soul's progress. It was not furnished, for Midmore was calculating how much it would cost to repave stables so dilapidated that even the village idiot apologised for putting visitors' horses into them. The man went away, and served up what he had heard of the pig-pound episode as a little newspaper sketch, calculated to annoy. Midmore read it with an eye as practical as a woman's, and since most of his experiences had been among women, at once sought out a woman to whom he might tell his sorrow at the disloyalty of his own familiar friend. She was so sympathetic that he went on to confide how his bruised heart – she knew all about it – had found so-lace, with a long O, in another quarter which he indicated rather carefully in case it might be betrayed to other loyal friends. As his hints pointed directly towards facile Hampstead, and as his urgent business was the purchase of a horse from a dealer, Beckenham way, he felt he had done good work. Later, when his friend, the scribe, talked to him alluringly of "secret gardens" and those so-laces to which every man who follows Wider Morality is entitled, Midmore lent him a five-pound note which he had got back on the price of a ninety-guinea bay gelding. So true it is, as he read in one of the late Colonel Werf's books, that "the young man of the present day would sooner lie under an imputation against his morals than against his knowledge of horse-flesh."

Midmore desired more than he desired anything else at that moment to ride and, above all, to jump on a ninety-guinea bay gelding with black points and a slovenly habit of hitting his fences. He did not wish many people except Mr. Sidney, who very kindly lent his soft meadow behind the flood-gates, to be privy to the matter, which he rightly foresaw would take him to the autumn. So he told such friends as hinted at country week-end visits that he had practically let his newly inherited house. The rent, he said, was an object to him, for he had lately lost large sums through ill-considered benevolences. He would name no names, but they could guess. And they guessed loyally all round the circle of his acquaintance as they spread the news that explained so much.

There remained only one couple of his once intimate associates to pacify. They were deeply sympathetic and utterly loyal, of course, but as curious as any of the apes whose diet they had adopted. Midmore met them in a sub-urban train, coming up to town, not twenty minutes after he had come off two hours' advanced tuition (one guinea an hour) over hurdles in a hall. He had, of course, changed his kit, but his too heavy bridle-hand shook a little among the newspapers. On the inspiration of the moment, which is your natural liar's best hold, he told them that he was con-demned to a rest-cure. He would lie in semi-darkness drink-ing milk, for weeks and weeks, cut off even from letters. He was astonished and delighted at the ease with which the usual lie confounds the unusual intellect. They swallowed it as swiftly as they recommended him to live on nuts and fruit; but he saw in the woman's eyes the exact reason she would set forth for his retirement. After all, she had as much right to express herself as he purposed to take for himself; and Midmore believed strongly in the fullest equality of the sexes.

That retirement made one small ripple in the strenuous world. The lady who had written the twelve-page letter ten months before sent him another of eight pages, analyzing all the motives that were leading her back to him – should she come? – now that he was ill and alone. Much might yet be retrieved, she said, out of the waste of jarring lives and piteous misunderstandings. It needed only a hand.

But Midmore needed two, next morning very early, for a devil's diversion, among wet coppices, called "cubbing."

"You haven't a bad seat," said Miss Sperrit through the morning-mist. "But you're worrying him."

"He pulls so," Midmore grunted.

"Let him alone, then. Look out for the branches," she shouted, as they whirled up a splashy ride. Cubs were plentiful. Most of the hounds attached themselves to a straight-necked youngster of education who scuttled out of the woods into the open fields below.

"Hold on!" some one shouted. "Turn 'em, Midmore. That's your brute Sidney's land. It's all wire."

"Oh, Connie, stop!" Mrs. Sperrit shrieked as her daughter charged at a boundary-hedge.

"Wire be damned! I had it all out a fortnight ago. Come on!" This was Midmore, buffeting into it a little lower down.

"*I* knew that!" Connie cried over her shoulder, and she flitted across the open pasture, humming to herself.

"Oh, of course! If some people have private information, they can afford to thrust." This was a snuff-coloured habit into which Miss Sperrit had cannoned down the ride.

"What! Midmore got Sidney to heel? *You* never did that, Sperrit." This was Mr. Fisher, M.F.H., enlarging the breach Midmore had made.

"No, confound him!" said the father testily. "Go on, sir! *Injecto ter pulvere* – you've kicked half the ditch into my eye already."

They killed that cub a little short of the haven his mother had told him to make for – a two-acre Alsatia of a gorse-patch to which the M.F.H. had been denied access for the last fifteen seasons. He expressed his gratitude before all the field and Mr. Sidney, at Mr. Sidney's farmhouse door.

"And if there should be any poultry claims – " he went on.

"There won't be," said Midmore. "It's too like cheating a sucking child, isn't it, Mr. Sidney?"

"You've got me!" was the reply. "I be used to bein' put upon, but you've got me, Mus' Midmore."

Midmore pointed to a new brick pig-pound built in strict disregard of the terms of the life-tenant's lease. The gesture told the tale to the few who did not know, and they shouted.

Such pagan delights as these were followed by pagan sloth of evenings when men and women elsewhere are at their brightest. But Midmore preferred to lie out on a yellow silk couch, reading works of a debasing vulgarity; or, by invitation, to dine with the Sperrits and savages of their kidney. These did not expect flights of fancy or phrasing. They lied, except about horses, grudgingly and of necessity, not for art's sake; and, men and women alike, they expressed themselves along their chosen lines with the serene indifference of the larger animals. Then Midmore would go home and identify them, one by one, out of the natural history books by Mr. Surtees, on the table beside the sofa. At first they looked upon him coolly, but when the tale of the removed wire and the recaptured gorse had gone the rounds, they accepted him for a person willing to play their games. True, a faction suspended judgment for a while, because they shot, and hoped that Midmore would serve the glorious mammon of pheasant-raising rather than the unkempt god of fox-hunting. But after he had shown his choice, they did not ask by what intellectual process he had arrived at it. He hunted three, sometimes four, times a week, which necessitated not only one bay gelding (£94 : 10s.), but a mannerly white-stockinged chestnut (£114), and a black mare, rather long in the back but with a mouth of silk (£150), who so evidently preferred to carry a lady that it would have been cruel to have baulked her. Besides, with that handling she could be sold at a profit. And besides, the hunt was a quiet, intimate, kindly little hunt, not anxious for strangers, of good report in the *Field*, the servant of one M.F.H., given to hospitality, riding well its own horses, and, with the exception of Midmore, not novices. But as Miss Sperrit observed, after the M.F.H. had said some things to him at a gate: "It *is* a pity you don't know as much as your horse, but you will in time. It takes years and yee-ars. I've been at it for fifteen and I'm only just learning. But you've made a decent kick-off."

So he kicked off in wind and wet and mud, wondering

quite sincerely why the bubbling ditches and sucking pastures held him from day to day, or what so-lace he could find on off days in chasing grooms and bricklayers round outhouses.

To make sure he up-rooted himself one week-end of heavy mid-winter rain, and re-entered his lost world in the character of Galahad fresh from a rest-cure. They all agreed, with an eye over his shoulder for the next comer, that he was a different man; but when they asked him for the symptoms of nervous strain, and led him all through their own, he realised he had lost much of his old skill in lying. His three months' absence, too, had put him hopelessly behind the London field. The movements, the allusions, the slang of the game had changed. The couples had rearranged themselves or were re-crystallizing in fresh triangles, whereby he put his foot in it badly. Only one great soul (he who had written the account of the pig-pound episode) stood untouched by the vast flux of time, and Midmore lent him another fiver for his integrity. A woman took him, in the wet forenoon, to a pronouncement on the Oneness of Impulse in Humanity, which struck him as a polysyllabic *résumé* of Mr. Sidney's domestic arrangements, plus a clarion call to "shock civilization into common-sense."

"And you'll come to tea with me to-morrow?" she asked, after lunch, nibbling cashew nuts from a saucer. Midmore replied that there were great arrears of work to overtake when a man has been put away for so long.

"But you've come back like a giant refreshed. ... I hope that Daphne" – this was the lady of the twelve and the eight-page letter – "will be with us too. She has misunderstood herself, like so many of us," the woman murmured, "but I think eventually..." she flung out her thin little hands. "However, these are things that each lonely soul must adjust for itself."

"Indeed, yes," said Midmore with a deep sigh. The old tricks were sprouting in the old atmosphere like mushrooms in a dung-pit. He passed into a abrupt reverie, shook his head, as though stung by tumultuous memories, and departed without any ceremony of farewell to – catch a mid-afternoon express where a man meets associates who talk

142

horse, and weather as it affects the horse, all the way down. What worried him most was that he had missed a day with the hounds.

He met Rhoda's keen old eyes without flinching; and the drawing-room looked very comfortable that wet evening at tea. After all, his visit to town had not been wholly a failure. He had burned quite a bushel of letters at his flat. A flat – here he reached mechanically toward the worn volumes near the sofa – a flat was a consuming animal. As for Daphne . . . he opened at random on the words: "His lordship then did as desired and disclosed a *tableau* of considerable strength and variety." Midmore reflected: "And I used to think . . . But she wasn't . . . We were all babblers and skirters together . . . I didn't babble much – thank goodness – but I skirted." He turned the pages backward for more *Sortes Surteesianae*, and read: "When at length they rose to go to bed it struck each man as he followed his neighbour upstairs, that the man before him walked very crookedly." He laughed aloud at the fire.

"What about to-morrow?" Rhoda asked, entering with garments over her shoulder. "It's never stopped raining since you left. You'll be plastered out of sight an' all in five minutes. You'd better wear your next best, 'adn't you? I'm afraid they've shrank. 'Adn't you best try 'em on?"

"Here?" said Midmore.

"'Suit yourself. I bathed you when you wasn't larger than a leg o' lamb," said the ex-ladies'-maid.

"Rhoda, one of these days I shall get a valet, and a married butler."

"There's many a true word spoke in jest. But nobody's huntin' to-morrow."

"Why? Have they cancelled the meet?"

"They say it only means slipping and over-reaching in the mud, and they all 'ad enough of that to-day. Charlie told me so just now."

"Oh!" It seemed that the word of Mr. Sperrit's confidential clerk had weight.

"Charlie came down to help Mr. Sidney lift the gates," Rhoda continued.

"The flood-gates? They are perfectly easy to handle now. I've put in a wheel and a winch."

"When the brook's really up they must be took clean out on account of the rubbish blockin' 'em. That's why Charlie came down."

Midmore grunted impatiently. "Everybody has talked to me about that brook ever since I came here. It's never done anything yet."

"This 'as been a dry summer. If you care to look now, sir, I'll get you a lantern."

She paddled out with him into a large wet night. Half-way down the lawn her light was reflected on shallow brown water, pricked through with grass blades at the edges. Beyond that light, the brook was strangling and kicking among hedges and tree-trunks.

"What on earth will happen to the big rose-bed?" was Midmore's first word.

"It generally 'as to be restocked after a flood. Ah!" she raised her lantern. "There's two garden-seats knockin' against the sun-dial. Now, that won't do the roses any good."

"This is too absurd. There ought to be some decently thought-out system – for – for dealing with this sort of thing." He peered into the rushing gloom. There seemed to be no end to the moisture and the racket. In town he had noticed nothing.

"It can't be 'elped," said Rhoda. "It's just what it does do once in just so often. We'd better go back."

All earth under foot was sliding in a thousand liquid noises towards the hoarse brook. Somebody wailed from the house: "'Fraid o' the water! Come 'ere! 'Fraid o' the water!"

"That's Jimmy. Wet always takes 'im that way," she explained. The idiot charged into them, shaking with terror.

"Brave Jimmy! How brave of Jimmy! Come into the hall. What Jimmy got now?" she crooned. It was a sodden note which ran: "Dear Rhoda – Mr. Lotten, with whom I rode home this afternoon, told me that if this wet keeps up, he's afraid the fish-pond he built last year, where Coxen's old mill-dam was, will go, as the dam did once before, he says. If it does it's bound to come down the brook. It may be all right, but perhaps you had better look out. C.S.'

"If Coxen's dam goes, that means . . . I'll 'ave the drawing-room carpet up at once to be on the safe side. The claw-'ammer is in the libery."

"Wait a minute. Sidney's gates are out, you said?"

"Both. He'll need it if Coxen's pond goes . . . I've seen it once."

"I'll just slip down and have a look at Sidney. Light the lantern again, please, Rhoda."

"You won't get *him* to stir. He's been there since he was born. But *she* don't know anything. I'll fetch your waterproof and some top-boots."

"'Fraid o' the water! 'Fraid o' the water!" Jimmy sobbed, pressed against a corner of the hall, his hands to his eyes.

"All right, Jimmy. Jimmy can help play with the carpet," Rhoda answered, as Midmore went forth into the darkness and the roarings all round. He had never seen such an utterly unregulated state of affairs. There was another lantern reflected on the streaming drive.

"Hi! Rhoda! Did you get my note? I came down to make sure. I thought, afterwards, Jimmy might funk the water!"

"It's me – Miss Sperrit," Midmore cried. "Yes, we got it, thanks."

"You're back, then. Oh, good! . . . It is bad down with you?"

"I'm going to Sidney's to have a look."

"You won't get *him* out. 'Lucky I met Bob Lotten. I told him he hadn't any business impounding water for his idiotic trout without rebuilding the dam."

"How far up is it? I've only been there once."

"Not more than four miles as the water will come. He says he's opened all the sluices."

She had turned and fallen into step beside him, her hooded head bowed against the thinning rain. As usual she was humming to herself.

"Why on earth did you come out in this weather?" Midmore asked.

"It was worse when you were in town. The rain's taking

145

off now. If it wasn't for that pond, I wouldn't worry so much. There's Sidney's bell. Come on!" She broke into a run. A cracked bell was jangling feebly down the valley.

"Keep on the road!" Midmore shouted. The ditches were snorting bank-full on either side, and towards the brook-side the fields were afloat and beginning to move in the darkness.

"Catch me going off it! There's his light burning all right." she halted undistressed at a little rise. "But the flood's in the orchard. Look!" She swung her lantern to show a front rank of old apple-trees reflected in still, out-lying waters beyond the half-drowned hedge. They could hear above the thud-thud of the gorged flood-gates, shrieks in two keys as monotonous as a steam-organ.

"The high one's the pig." Miss Sperrit laughed.

"All right! I'll get *her* out. You stay where you are, and I'll see you home afterwards."

"But the water's only just over the road," she objected.

"Never mind. Don't you move. Promise?"

"All right. You take my stick, then, and feel for holes in case anything's washed out anywhere. This *is* a lark!"

Midmore took it, and stepped into the water that moved sluggishly as yet across the farm road which ran to Sidney's front door from the raised and metalled public road. It was half way up to his knees when he knocked. As he looked back Miss Sperrit's lantern seemed to float in mid-ocean.

"You can't come in or the water'll come with you. I've bunged up all the cracks," Mr. Sidney shouted from within. "Who be ye?"

"Take me out! Take me out!" the woman shrieked, and the pig from his sty behind the house urgently seconded the motion.

"I'm Midmore! Coxen's old mill-dam is likely to go, they say. Come out!"

"I told 'em it would when they made a fish-pond of it. 'Twasn't ever puddled proper. But it's a middlin' wide valley. She's got room to spread ... Keep still, or I'll take and duck you in the cellar! .. You go 'ome, Mus' Midmore, an' take the law o' Mus' Lotten soon's you've changed your socks."

"Confound you, aren't you coming out?"

"To catch me death o' cold? I'm all right where I be. I've seen it before. But you can take *her*. She's no sort o' use or sense . . . Climb out through the window. Didn't I tell you I'd plugged the door-cracks, you fool's daughter?" The parlour window opened, and the woman flung herself into Midmore's arms, nearly knocking him down. Mr. Sidney leaned out of the window, pipe in mouth.

"Take her 'ome," he said, and added oracularly:

"Two women in one house,
Two cats an' one mouse,
Two dogs an' one bone –
Which I will leave alone.

I've seen it before." Then he shut and fastened the window.

"A trap! A trap! You had ought to have brought a trap for me. I'll be drowned in this wet," the woman cried.

"Hold up! You can't be any wetter than you are. Come along!" Midmore did not at all like the feel of the water over his boot-tops.

"Hooray! Come along!" Miss Sperrit's lantern, not fifty yards away, waved cheerily.

The woman threshed towards it like a panic-striken goose, fell on her knees, was jerked up again by Midmore, and pushed on till she collapsed at Miss Sperrit's feet.

"But you won't get bronchitis if you go straight to Mr. Midmore's house," said the unsympathetic maiden.

"O Gawd! O Gawd! I wish our 'eavenly Father 'ud forgive me my sins an' call me 'ome," the women sobbed. "But I won't go to '*is* 'ouse! I won't."

"All right, then. Stay here. Now, if we run," Miss Sperrit whispered to Midmore, "she'll follow us. Not too fast!"

They set off at a considerate trot, and the woman lumbered behind them, bellowing, till they met a third lantern – Rhoda holding Jimmy's hand. She had got the carpet up, she said, and was escorting Jummy past the water that he dreaded.

"That's all right," Miss Sperrit pronounced. "Take Mrs. Sidney back with you, Rhoda, and put her to bed. I'll take Jimmy with me. You aren't afraid of the water now, are you, Jimmy?"

"Not afraid of anything now." Jimmy reached for her hand. "But get away from the water quick."

"I'm coming with you," Midmore interrupted.

"You most certainly are not. You're drenched. She threw you twice. Go home and change. You may have to be out again all night. It's only half-past seven now. I'm perfectly safe." She flung herself lightly over a stile, and hurried uphill by the footpath, out of reach of all but the boasts of the flow below.

Rhoda, dead silent, herded Mrs. Sidney to the house."

"You'll find your things laid out on the bed," she said to Midmore as he came up. 'I'll attend to – to this. *She*'s got nothing to cry for."

Midmore raced into dry kit, and raced uphill to be rewarded by the sight of the lantern just turning into the Sperrits' gate. He came back by way of Sidney's farm, where he saw the light twinkling across three acres of shining water, for the rain had ceased and the clouds were stripping overhead, though the brook was noisier than ever. Now there was only that doubtful mill-pond to look after – that and his swirling world abandoned to himself alone.

"We shall have to sit up for it," said Rhoda after dinner. And as the drawing-room commanded the best view of the rising flood, they watched it from there for a long time, while all the clocks of the house bore them company.

"'Tisn't the water, it's the mud on the skirting-board after it goes down that I mind," Rhoda whispered. "The last time Coxen's mill broke, I remember it came up to the second – no, third – step o' Mr. Sidney's stairs."

"What did Sidney do about it?"

"He made a notch on the step. 'E said it was a record. Just like 'im."

"It's up to the drive now," said Midmore after another long wait. "And the rain stopped before eight, you know."

"Then Coxen's dam 'as broke, and that's the first of the

flood-water." She stared out beside him. The water was rising in sudden pulses – an inch or two at a time, with great sweeps and lagoons and a sudden increase of the brook's proper thunder.

"You can't stand all the time. Take a chair," Midmore said presently.

Rhoda looked back into the bare room. "The carpet bein' up *does* make a difference. Thank you, sir, I *will* 'ave a set-down."

"'Right over the drive now," said Midmore. He opened the window and leaned out. "Is that wind up the valley, Rhoda?"

"No, that's *it*! But I've seen it before."

There was not so much a roar as the purposeful drive of a tide across a jagged reef, which put down every other sound for twenty minutes. A wide sheet of water hurried up to the little terrace on which the house stood, pushed round either corner, rose again and stretched, as it were, yawning beneath the moonlight, joined other sheets waiting for them in unsuspected hollows, and lay out all in one. A puff of wind followed.

"It's right up to the wall now. I can touch it with my finger." Midmore bent over the window-sill.

"I can 'ear it in the cellars," said Rhoda dolefully. "Well, we've done what we can! I think I'll 'ave a look." She left the room and was absent half an hour or more, during which time he saw a full-grown tree hauling itself across the lawn by its naked roots. Then a hurdle knocked against the wall, caught on an iron foot-scraper just outside, and made a square-headed ripple. The cascade through the cell-windows diminished.

"It's dropping," Rhoda cried, as she returned. "It's only tricklin' into my cellars now."

"Wait a minute. I believe – I believe I can see the scraper on the edge of the drive just showing!"

In another ten minutes the drive itself roughened and became gravel again, tilting all its water towards the shrubbery.

"The pond's gone past," Rhoda announced. "We shall

149

only 'ave the common flood to contend with now. You'd better go to bed."

"I ought to go down and have another look at Sidney before daylight."

"No need. You can see 'is light burnin' from all the upstairs windows."

"By the way. I forgot about *her*. Where've you put her?"

"In my bed." Rhoda's tone was ice. "I wasn't going to undo a room for *that* stuff."

"But it – it couldn't be helped," said Midmore. 'She was half drowned. One mustn't be narrow-minded, Rhoda, even if her position isn't quite – er – regular."

"Pfff! I wasn't worryin' about that." She leaned forward to the window. "There's the edge of the lawn showin' now. It falls as fast as it rises. Dearie" – the change of tone made Midmore jump – "didn't you know that I was 'is first? *That's* what makes it so hard to bear." Midmore looked at the long lizard-like back and had no words.

She went on, still talking through the black window-pane: "Your pore dear auntie was very kind about it. She said she'd make all allowances for one, but no more. Never any more ... Then, you didn't know 'oo Charlie was all this time?"

"Your nephew, I always thought."

"Well, well," she spoke pityingly. "Everybody's business being nobody's business, I suppose no one thought to tell you. But Charlie made 'is own way for 'imself from the beginnin'! ... But *her* upstairs, she never produced anything. Just an 'ousekeeper, as you might say. 'Turned over an' went to sleep straight off. She 'ad the impudence to ask me for 'ot sherry-gruel."

"Did you give it to her," said Midmore.

"Me? Your sherry? No!"

The memory of Sidney's outrageous rhyme at the window, and Charlie's long nose (he thought it looked interested at the time) as he passed the copies of Mrs. Werf's last four wills, overcame Midmore without warning.

"This damp is givin' you a cold," said Rhoda, rising. "There you go again! Sneezin's a sure sign of it. Better go to

150

bed. You can't do anythin' excep'" she stood rigid, with crossed arms – "about me."

"Well. What about you?" Midmore stuffed the handkerchief in his pocket.

"Now you know about it, what are you goin' to do – sir?" She had the answer on her lean cheek before the sentence was finished.

"Go and see if you can get us something to eat, Rhoda. And beer."

"I expec' the larder 'll be in a swim," she replied, "but old bottled stuff don't take any harm from wet." She returned with a tray, all in order, and they ate and drank together, and took observations of the falling flood till dawn opened its bleared eyes on the wreck of what had been a fair garden. Midmore, cold and annoyed, found himself humming:

> "That flood strewed wrecks upon the grass,
> That ebb swept out the flocks to sea.

There isn't a rose left, Rhoda!

> An awesome ebb and flow it was
> To many more than mine and me.
> But each will mourn his . . .

It'll cost me a hundred."

"Now we know the worst," said Rhoda, "we can go to bed. I'll lay on the kitchen sofa. His light's burnin' still."

"And *she*?"

"Dirty old cat! You ought to 'ear 'er snore!"

At ten o'clock in the morning, after a maddening hour in his own garden on the edge of the retreating brook, Midmore went off to confront more damage at Sidney's. The first thing that met him was the pig, snowy white, for the water had washed him out of his new sty, calling on high heaven for breakfast. The front door had been forced open, and the flood had registered its own height in a brown dado on the walls. Midmore chased the pig out and called up the stairs.

151

"I be abed o' course. Which step 'as she rose to?" Sidney cried from above. "The fourth? Then it's beat all records. Come up."

"Are you ill?" Midmore asked as he entered the room. The red eyelids blinked cheerfully. Mr. Sidney, beneath a sumptuous patch-work quilt, was smoking.

"Nah! I'm only thankin' God I ain't my own landlord. Take that cheer. What's she done?"

"It hasn't gone down enough for me to make sure."

"Them floodgates o' yourn 'll be middlin' far down the brook by now; an' your rose-garden have gone after 'em. I saved my chickens, though. You'd better get Mus' Sperrit to take the law o' Lotten an' 'is fish-pond."

"No, thanks. I've trouble enough without that."

"Hev ye?" Mr. Sidney grinned. "How did ye make out with those two women o' mine last night? I lay they fought."

"You infernal old scoundrel!" Midmore laughed.

"I be – an' then again I bain't," was the placid answer. "But, Rhoda, *she* wouldn't ha' left me last night. Fire or flood, she wouldn't.'

"Why didn't you ever marry her?" Midmore asked.

"Waste of good money. She was willin' without."

There was a step on the gritty mud below and a voice humming. Midmore rose quickly saying: "Well, I suppose you're all right now."

"I be. I ain't a landlord, nor I ain't young – nor anxious. Oh. Mus' Midmore! Would it make any odds about her thirty pounds comin' regular if I married her? Charlie said maybe 'twould."

"Did he?" Midmore turned at the door. "And what did Jimmy say about it?"

"Jimmy?" Mr. Sidney chuckled as the joke took him. "Oh, *he's* none o' mine. He's Charlie's look-out."

Midmore slammed the door and ran downstairs.

"Well, this is a – sweet – mess," said Miss Sperrit in shortest skirts and heaviest riding-boots. "I had to come down and have a look at it. 'The old mayor climbed the belfry tower.' 'Been up all night nursing your family?'

"Nearly that! Isn't it cheerful?" He pointed through the

152

door to the stairs with small twig-drift on the last three treads.

"It's a record, though," she said, and hummed to herself:

"That flood strewed wrecks upon the grass,
That ebb swept out the flocks to sea.'

"You're always singing that, aren't you?" Midmore said suddenly as she passed into the parlour where slimy chairs had been stranded at all angles.

"Am I? Now I come to think of it I believe I do. They say I always hum when I ride. Have you noticed it?"

"Of course I have. I notice every – "

"Oh," she went on hurriedly. "We had it for the village cantata last winter – 'The Brides of Enderby.' "

"No! 'High Tide on the Coast of Lincolnshire.' " For some reason Midmore spoke sharply.

"Just like that." She pointed to the befouled walls. "I say ... Let's get this furniture a little straight ... You know it too?"

"Every word, since you sang it, of course."

"When?"

"The first night I ever came down. You rode past the drawing-room window in the dark singing it – 'And sweeter woman – ' "

"I thought the house was empty then. Your aunt always let us use that short cut. Ha-hadn't we better get this out into the passage? It'll all have to come out anyhow. You take the other side." They began to lift a heavyish table. Their words came jerkily between gasps and their faces were as white as – a newly washed and very hungry pig.

"Look out!" Midmore shouted. His legs were whirled from under him, as the table, grunting madly, careened and knocked the girl out of sight.

The wild boar of Asia could not have cut down a couple more scientifically, but this little pig lacked his ancestor's nerve and fled shrieking over their bodies.

"Are you hurt, darling?" was Midmore's first word, and "No – I'm only winded – dear." was Miss Sperrit's, as he

153

lifted her out of her corner, her hat over one eye and her right cheek a smear of mud.

*   *   *

They fed him a little later on some chicken-feed that they found in Sidney's quiet barn, a pail of buttermilk out of the dairy, and a quantity of onions from a shelf in the back-kitchen.

"Seed-onions, most likely," said Connie. "You'll hear about this."

"What does it matter? They ought to have been gilded. We must buy him."

"And keep him as long as he lives," she agreed. "But I think I ought to go home now. You see, when I came out I didn't expect . . . Did you?"

"No! Yes . . . It had to come . . . But if any one had told me an hour ago! . . . Sidney's unspeakable parlour – and the mud on the carpet."

"Oh, I say! Is my cheek clean now?"

"Not quite. Lend me your hanky again a minute, darling. . . . What a purler you came!"

"You can't talk. 'Remember when your chin hit that table and you said 'blast'! I was just going to laugh."

"You didn't laugh when I picked you up. You were going 'oo-oo-oo' like a little owl."

"My dear child – "

"Say that again!"

"My dear child. (Do you really like it? I keep it for my best friends.) My *dee-ar* child, I thought I was going to be sick there and then. He knocked every ounce of wind out of me – the angel! But I must really go."

They set off together, very careful not to join hands or take arms.

"Not across the fields," said Midmore at the stile. "Come round by – by your own place."

She flushed indignantly.

"It will be yours in a little time," he went on, shaken with his own audacity.

"Not so much of your little times, if you please!" she shied like a colt across the road; then instantly, like a colt, her eyes lit with new curiosity as she came in sight of the drive-gates.

"And not quite so much of your airs and graces, Madam," Midmore returned, "or I won't let you use our drive as a short cut any more."

"Oh, I'll be good. I'll be good." Her voice changed suddenly. "I swear I'll try to be good, dear. I'm not much of a thing at the best. What made *you* ..."

"I'm worse – worse! Miles and oceans worse. But what does it matter now?"

They halted beside the gate-pillars.

"I see!" she said, looking up the sodden carriage sweep to the front door porch where Rhoda was slapping a wet mat to and fro. "*I* see ... Now, I really must go home. No! Don't you come. I must speak to Mother first all by myself."

He watched her up the hill till she was out of sight

IN PARTIBUS

It's Oh for one deep whisky-peg
   When Christmas winds are blowing,
When all the men you ever knew,
   And all you've ceased from knowing,
Are "entered for the Tournament,
   And everything that's going".

But I consort with long-haired things
   In velvet collar-rolls,
Who talk about the Aims of Art,
   And "theories" and "goals",
And moo and coo with womenfolk
   About their blessed souls.

155

But that they call "psychology"
  Is lack of liver-pill,
And all that blights their tender souls
  Is eating till they're ill,
And their chief way of winning goals
  Consists of sitting still.

Its Oh to meet an Army man,
  Set up, and trimmed and taut,
Who does not spout hashed libraries
  Or think the next man's thought,
And walks as though he owned himself,
  And hogs his bristles short.

Hear now a voice across the seas
  To kin beyond my ken,
If ye have ever filled an hour
  With stories from my pen,
For pity's sake send some one here
  To bring me news of men!

OTHER BOOKS FROM MARLBOROUGH AVAILABLE NOW